CATALOGUE
OF THE CARVED AMBER

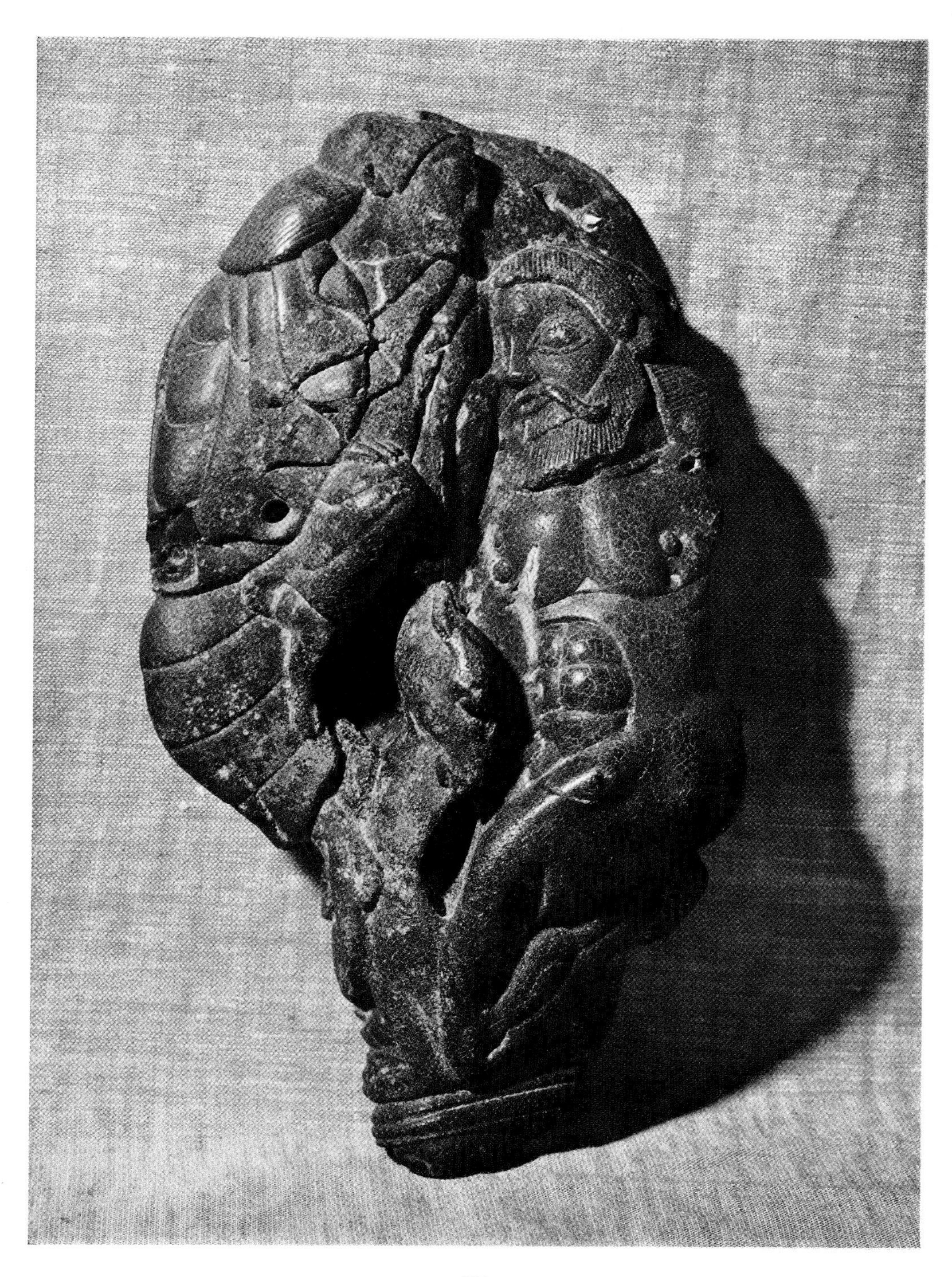

35

[*Frontispiece*

CATALOGUE OF THE
CARVED AMBER

IN THE
DEPARTMENT OF
GREEK AND ROMAN ANTIQUITIES

by

D. E. STRONG
Assistant Keeper of Greek and Roman Antiquities

LONDON
THE TRUSTEES OF THE BRITISH MUSEUM
1966

PRINTED AND BOUND IN ENGLAND BY
HAZELL WATSON AND VINEY LTD
AYLESBURY, BUCKS

To the memory of
PAUL JACOBSTHAL

PREFACE

In *Archäologisches Anzeiger* 1928 the late Paul Jacobsthal announced his work on ancient amber carvings and called for information about examples in lesser-known collections. The response to this request was a most generous and fruitful one, and by the time of his death he had built up a considerable 'dossier' of letters, photographs, and notes which was kept, and is still available, in the Department of Greek and Roman Antiquities. Jacobsthal was also intending to produce a catalogue of the large collection of ancient ambers in the British Museum and he had prepared notes and sketches of most of the 'Italic' pieces in which he was especially interested. These notes are also in the Department. In preparing this catalogue I have not made a great deal of use of Jacobsthal's German notes on the collection which are written in pencil in a minute and difficult hand and consist only of basic descriptions. But the comparative material he had collected over the years has proved invaluable, and it is hoped that the dedication of this Catalogue to his memory will be some recognition of his work.

Part of the manuscript of this catalogue has been read by Dr J. Gy. Szilagyi, to whom I am grateful for help on a number of questions. My colleague Dr. R. A. Higgins has kindly read the proofs. Miss M. O. Miller drew the maps, figs. 1 and 2.

D. E. S.

CONTENTS

ABBREVIATIONS

The abbreviations for periodicals referred to in this Catalogue are those recommended in *Journal of Hellenic Studies*, vol. lxvii, p. xxii f. and *Annual of the British School at Athens*, vol. 44, 333 ff. Other periodicals and books referred to in the text are abbreviated as follows:

Åberg, *Chronologie* = N. Åberg, *Bronzezeitliche und früheisenzeitliche Chronologie*, 1930–3.

Artemis Orthia = R. M. Dawkins (ed.), *The Sanctuary of Artemis Orthia at Sparta*, 1929.

Bauer-Schlossmacher = M. Bauer, *Edelsteinkunde* (3rd edition by Schlossmacher), 1932.

BABesch = *Bulletin van de Vereeniging tot Bevordering der Kennis van de antieke Beschaving.*

Becatti, *Oreficerie* = G. Becatti, *Oreficerie antiche dalle Minoiche alle Barbariche*, 1955.

Beck, *Beads and Pendants* = H. C. Beck, 'Classification and Nomenclature of Beads and Pendants', in *Archaeologia* lxxvii, 1928.

Blinkenberg, *Fibules* = C. Blinkenberg, *Fibules grecques et orientales*, 1926.

Blümner, *Technologie* = H. Blümner, *Technologie und Terminologie der Gewerbe und Künste bei Griechen und Römern*, 1875–1887.

Boardman, *Cretan Collection* = J. Boardman, *The Cretan Collection in Oxford*, 1961.

Civiltà del Ferro = *Civiltà del Ferro, Studi pubblicati nella ricorrenza centenaria della scoperta di Villanova*, Bologna, 1960.

Detken, *Ambers* = A. Detken, *Ambers found in Canosa in 1812*.

Doelter-Leitmeier = C. Doelter and H. Leitmeier, *Handbuch der Mineralchemie*, 4 vols., 1912–31.

Dohan, *Tomb Groups* = E. H. Dohan, *Italic Tomb Groups*, 1942.

Evans, *P. of M.* = Sir Arthur Evans, *The Palace of Minos at Knossos*, 4 vols. from 1921.

Falchi, *Vetulonia* = I. Falchi, *Vetulonia e la sua necropoli antichissima*, 1892.

Giglioli = G. Q. Giglioli, *L'Arte Etrusca*, 1935.

GJ = *Geographical Journal.*

Gjerstad, *Early Rome* = E. Gjerstad. *Early Rome*, Vol. I (1953), II (1956), III (1960).

Gozzadini, *Ulteriori scoperte* = G. Gozzadini, *Di ulteriori scoperte nell' antica necropoli a Marzabotto nel Bolognese*. 1870.

Guida Ancona = *Guida illustrata del Museo Nazionale di Ancona*, 1915.

Hogarth, *Ephesus* = D. G. Hogarth, *Excavations at Ephesus*, Text and Atlas, 1908.

ILN = *Illustrated London News.*

JRGZM = *Jahrbuch des römisch-germanischen Zentralmuseums, Mainz.*

Karo, *Schachtgräber* = G. Karo, *Die Schachtgräber von Mykenai*, 1930–33.
Kerameikos = *Kerameikos, Ergebnisse der Ausgrabungen*, 6 vols., from 1939.
Minto, *Populonia* = A. Minto, *Populonia, la necropoli arcaica*, 1922.
Montelius = O. Montelius, *La civilisation primitive en Italie*, 2 vols., 1895.
Olympia = E. Curtius and F. Adler, *Olympia*, 5 vols., from 1897.
Ori e Argenti = *Ori e Argenti dell'Italia Antica* (Catalogue of Exhibition in Turin, 1961).
Pareti = L. Pareti, *La Tomba Regolini-Galassi*, 1947.
Pauly-Wissowa = *Paulys Real-Encyclopädie der classischen Altertumswissenschaft.*
Pelka, *Bernstein* = O. Pelka, *Bernstein*, 1920.
Perachora i and ii = *Perachora, The Sanctuaries of Hera Akraia and Limenia*, vol. I, 1940, vol. II, 1962.
Persson, *Royal Tombs* = A. W. Persson, *Royal Tombs at Dendra near Midea*, 1931.
Persson, *New Tombs* = A. W. Persson, *New Tombs at Dendra near Midea*, 1942.
Pinza, *Materiali* = G. Pinza, *Materiali per la Etnologia Antica Toscano-Laziale*, 1915.
PPS = Proceedings of the Prehistoric Society.
de Ridder = A. de Ridder, *Musée National du Louvre, Catalogue sommaire des bijoux antiques*, 1924.
Richter, *Etruscan Collection* = G. M. A. Richter, *Handbook of the Etruscan Collection*, 1940.
Rostovtzeff, *SEHRE* = M. Rostovtzeff, *The Social and Economic History of the Roman Empire*, 2nd. ed., 1957.
Siviero = R. Siviero, *Gli ori e le ambre del Museo Nazionale di Napoli*, 1954.
Sundwall = J. Sundwall, *Die älteren italischen Fibeln*, 1943.
Trebenischte = B. D. Filow and K. Schkorpil, *Die archaische Nekropole von Trebenischte*, 1927.
Wace, *Chamber Tombs* = A. J. B. Wace, *Chamber Tombs at Mycenae* (*Archaeologia*, vol. lxxxii), 1932.
Zannoni, *Certosa* = A. Zannoni, *Gli scavi della Certosa di Bologna*, 1876.
ZfE = *Zeitschrift für Ethnologie.*

INTRODUCTION

I. VARIETIES OF AMBER

Amber is the fossilised resin of extinct coniferous trees. It is obtained chiefly from the coasts of the Baltic, especially the peninsula of Samland on the east side of the Gulf of Danzig, but varieties of amber, differing from one another in colour and chemical composition, are found in many other parts of the world. The main varieties may be briefly described as follows:

a. *Baltic amber* is found washed up from submarine strata on the coasts of the E. Baltic;[1] it is also mined from lower oligocene beds, known as the 'Blue Earth', on the Samland peninsula.[2] The chemical composition (formula $C_{10}H_{16}O$) varies slightly; it contains an average of 79% carbon, 10·5% oxygen and 10·5% hydrogen, with some sulphur and a little inorganic material. Its specific gravity is 1·05–1·10 and its hardness is 2–2·5, i.e. it is slightly heavier than water and harder than most resins. By distillation, oil of amber and succinic acid, both of which are given off as fumes, may be separated; the quantity of succinic acid varies—clear specimens are said to have 3–4%, cloudy approximately 8%.[3] Amber melts between 600° and 615° fahr. As it is heated in the air it softens and swells, and it burns with a bright sooty flame. It is completely amorphous and non-crystalline and is found in irregular rounded lumps sometimes penetrated by deep cracks. The natural colour ranges from pale yellow to brown and it may be transparent or cloudy.[4] With time it usually changes colour to red or brownish red as a result of atmospheric weathering and the surface becomes cracked.[5] Other colours, e.g. green and blue, also occur. The amber which is found in quantity on the coast of W. Jutland and Schleswig Holstein and sporadically on the E. coast of England in Norfolk and Suffolk has the same chemical composition as the Baltic amber. This northern amber is known generically as *succinite*.

b. *Sicilian amber* is found washed down at the mouths of a number of Sicilian rivers, especially the Simeto near Catania. Its chemical composition is somewhat different from Baltic amber; it contains a higher proportion of sulphur[6] (as much

1. For a map showing the distribution of Baltic amber, F. Kaunhowen in *Jahrb.d.preuss. Geol.* vol. 34, ii, 1913.
2. See table of deposits in Bauer-Schlossmacher.
3. For the succinic acid test see below pp. 5–6.
4. The varieties and trade-names of Baltic amber are listed in Bauer-Schlossmacher, p.p. 706–21.
5. See below pp. 15–16.
6. The test of fluorescence (see p. 7) is based on the presence of sulphur.

as 2·46% in some examples) and no succinic acid. It also seems to be rather softer and is found in a much greater variety of natural colours. The normal colour is reddish-yellow to wine red, sometimes so dark as to seem almost black; blue and green examples are also found.[1]

c. *Rumanian amber* is found in Miocene strata, especially on the river Buźau; it is also mined in limestone beds by the river. Its structure, density and chemical composition are very similar to Baltic amber. There is always 1–5% of succinic acid and about 1·10% of sulphur; it is slightly denser and melts at a rather higher temperature. It occurs in a rich variety of colours—yellow, reds of different tone, grey, blue and black; it is generally transparent with an opaque crust, darker in colour than the inside.

d. *Burmese amber* is found in clay beds on a range of hills near Maingkwan in the upper reaches of the Chindwin river. Its chemical composition is similar to Baltic amber but it is harder and contains less succinic acid. The colour range is from light yellow to dark brown.[2]

e. *Other varieties.* It is not proposed to list in detail the other varieties of amber but two resins, neither of which is properly amber, should be mentioned here, since both were available in ancient times. A fossil resin is found in the Apennines which have been thought of as a source of ancient amber; it is not true succinite.[3] A similar resin is found in the Lebanon, not far from Sidon. Examples collected by O. Fraas[4] and submitted to tests were shown to contain no succinic acid.[5] In appearance it is very like succinite but it is extremely brittle and only suitable for making small beads.

Specimens of the best-known varieties of amber may be seen in the Geological Museum at South Kensington (*Guide to the Collection of Gemstones in the Geological Museum*, H.M.S.O., 1951, pp. 56–7.)

Bibliography

Bauer-Schlossmacher pp. 706–21
L. Schmid in Doelter-Leitmeier, iv, iii, & pp. 842 ff.
K. Andrée, *Der Bernstein und seine Bedeutung*, 1937.
K. Andrée, *Bernsteinforschungen*, 1929–39.
K. Andrée, *Der Bernstein, das Bernsteinland und sein Leben*, 1951.
G. C. Williamson, *A book of amber*, 1932.
O. C. Farrington, *Amber*, 1927.
M. Ebert(ed), *Reallexikon der Vorgeschichte*, 1924–9.
W. A. Buffum, *The Tears of the Heliades*, 1900.

1. The wide variety of colours in Sicilian amber is described and illustrated in W. A. Buffum's *The Tears of the Heliades*, London, 1900.
2. N. M. Penzer, *The Mineral Resources of Burma*, London, 1922, p. 38 ff.
3. See Doelter-Leitmeier, p. 936, and O. Olshausen and F. Rathgen 'Untersuchungen über baltischen Bernstein (Succinit) und andere fossile Bernsteinähnliche Harze' in *ZfE*, 1904, pp. 153–63.
4. *Drei Monate am Libanon*, Stuttgart, 1876, p. 67 and 94, note 2.
5. Doelter-Leitmeier, p. 936 ff., includes Syrian amber in the category of 'Bernsteinähnliche Harze'.

II. ANCIENT NAMES FOR AMBER

The Greek word for amber was ἤλεκτρος or ἤλεκτρον. It is used in the Odyssey where it means both amber and electrum, the alloy of gold and silver; neither the gender of the word nor the meaning is always clear but amber is certainly referred to in *Odyssey* xv 460[1] and xviii 295. It is possible, but it cannot be proved, that in the early poets the masculine form of the word = electrum and the neuter = amber;[2] in Herodotus and in Aristotle the word is neuter when it means amber and in Pausanias the words for both electrum and amber are neuter. Hesychius (s.v. ἤλεκτρος) makes the word for amber masculine, but the text is confusing. When used in the plural, as it frequently is in a generic sense, the word always means amber.

The Roman word for amber was *sucinum*, often, like the Greek word, used in the plural (e.g. Pliny *NH* xxxvii 30). *Electrum*, a transliteration of the Greek word is commonly used, expecially by Pliny when referring to Greek sources, and often by the Latin poets. Conversely, the word σουκίνος from the Latin appears in later Greek texts.[3] Pliny[4] and Tacitus[5] both mention a Germanic word for amber latinised into *glaesum*, whence *insulae glaesariae*.

III. ANCIENT SOURCES

> inde fluunt lacrimae, stillataque sole rigescunt
> de ramis electra novis, quae lucidus amnis
> excipit et nuribus mittit gestanda Latinis
>
> Ovid *Met.* ii,, 364 ff.

Much has been written by the Greeks and Romans themselves and much more by modern scholars about the sources of the amber used in antiquity. The Greek legend, which is told in full by Ovid and for which Pliny quotes among others Aeschylus, Euripides[6] and Satyrus, tells how the tears of the sisters of Phaethon as they wept for the death of their brother, were hardened by the sun and became lumps of amber. The river of the myth was the Eridanos which flowed into the northern sea, and it was later identified with a number of rivers known to the Greeks; Pherecydes seems to have been the first to express the view, which was widely accepted later, that the Eridanos was the Po. The more cautious Herodotus,[7] writing at a time when amber was little known in the Greek world, prefers scepticism. This ancient identification of the Eridanos with the Po, and the vast quantities

1. χρύσεον ὅρμον ἔχων, μετὰ δ' ἠλέκροίσιν ἔερτο
2. In Hesiod *Scut. Herc.* 141 ἤλεκτρον is used where it very probably means amber.
3. Artemidorus II, 5, Suidas s.v.
4. *NH* xxxvii, 42.
5. *Germania* 45.
6. Hippolytus 732–41.
7. iii, 115.

of amber found on Italian Iron Age sites has led to the belief current in recent times that North and Central Italy, especially the area round Ravenna and Bologna, was an ancient source of natural amber. But, in fact, the fossil resin which has been identified in this area is not true amber, and, in any case, the yield is said to be extremely small. The arguments of Capellini that the worked ambers found in the Bolognese are from local sources[1] were refuted by Helbig. It is much more likely that the identification of the Eridanos with the Po arose from the importance of the river valley at the head of the amber route, a fact which is amply proved for classical times by the finds of amber in sixth and fifth century graves at Spina, the Etruscan trading station at the mouth of the Po.

More reliable details about the methods of winning amber began to be known in the fourth century B.C. Aristotle[2] was able to give a fairly precise description of the processes by which amber was formed and several other writers have knowledge, usually at second or third hand, of its geographical distribution. The fourth-century geographer Pytheas[3] referred to the island of Abalus where amber was washed in up the spring and a similar account appears in Diodorus,[4] following Timaeus, who calls the island Basileia. This island is also mentioned by Pliny[5]; it lay off the Jutland peninsula which was always an important source, though not, in Roman times, the principal source of amber.

When Diodorus wrote, amber was reaching the classical world only in very small quantities and knowledge of it was gained at second-hand. In later Roman times however Tacitus shows direct knowledge of the methods of acquiring amber among the Aestii of the Baltic coast and he gives an account of them.[6] Pliny makes it clear that the main source of amber used in Italy in Roman times was the Baltic coast; by his time an enterprising trader had reached the amber coast, and, probably for the first time in antiquity, established direct trade with the natives.[7] Pliny also mentions other varieties—from India and Syria—but he does not say that they were used by the Romans.

There is, in fact, no evidence that any possible sources of amber apart from the northern ones were exploited in Roman times. The nearest is, of course, Sicily and it might be expected that Sicilian amber was known and used in ancient times. But it is never mentioned, not even by Diodorus who should have known about it. Modern scholars have inferred that much of the Italic amber came from this source

1. *Sitzungsberichte der Berliner Gesellschaft für Anthropologie,* 1872; see also *Congrès International d'Anthropologie et d'Archéologie Préhistorique, C. Rend. de la 7 session,* Stockholm, 1874, p. 777 ff. On the origins of Italian amber see also *SE* iii. 427 ff., xvii, 32 ff., xvii, 419 ff.

2. *Animal. Gener.* ii, 736a, 5. 3. Pliny *NH* xxxvii, 35. 4. v, 23. 5. *NH* xxxvii, 35.

6. *Germania* 45; ergo iam dextro Suebici maris litore Aestiorum gentes alluuntur . . . sed et mare scrutantur, ac soli omnium sucinum, quod ipsi glaesum vocant, inter vada atque in ipso litore legunt.

7. *NH* xxxvii, 45; DC mil. p. fere a Carnunto Pannoniae abesse litus id Germaniae ex quo invehitur percognitum est nuper . . .

or from deposits in Central Italy, but there seems to be nothing to support the theory. The succinic acid test, which is discussed below, seems to show that most of the ancient amber is succinite, and, therefore, from northern sources; the supplies in Rumania and further afield seem never to have been tapped. 'Amber' from Syria, which is known to Pliny, may have been used locally and it is interesting that in the description of Roman Syria (Ta Tsin) in the annals of the Han Dynasty, based on an account of Kan Yang (A.D. 97) amber is mentioned as one of the products.[1] Ambers of the Roman period which are probably local products have been found in Palestine and Syria but none have been submitted to tests in order to discover the origin of the raw material.

The substance λιγγούριον or λυγγούριον (Lat. lyncurium) is frequently referred to in modern discussions of the ancient sources of amber. The earliest reference to this substance is in *IG* XI, no. 161, B 49, a third century B.C. temple inventory from Delos in which it appears to be used for a ring or seal-stone. While Plutarch[2] says it was formed from the urine of the lynx, Strabo[3] who calls it λιγγούριον says it comes from Liguria, a fact which explains its name, and adds that some people call it *electrum*. Hesychius glosses the word with τὸ ἤλεκτρον. In Pliny's day the view seems to have been widely held that it was, in fact, a kind of amber, though Pliny himself considers it to be purely mythical. Schulten[4] has tried to show that in antiquity Jutland was called the Ligurian coast so that λιγγούριον could indeed be an alternative to ἤλεκτρον. Whatever the truth about this material may be, no natural amber nor any substance with similar properties has ever been found in areas covered by ancient Liguria nor does Liguria ever seem to have been an important entrepôt in the amber trade.

Apart from the ancient literary sources which, when they may be relied upon, are unequivocal in attributing amber to northern sources, further evidence may be obtained from the chemical tests which have been applied to amber in order to discover its origin. The most effective seems to be the succinic acid test (see table, p. 6). Although there is no absolute agreement among scientists as to the precise quantity of this acid present in the various kinds of amber, generally speaking, Sicilian (and Syrian) amber has a very low content (rarely more than ·4%) while Baltic amber never has less than 3% and may have as much as 8%. Helm stated categorically[5] that the test distinguishes Baltic from Sicilian amber and if this is so, the tests seem to confirm the Baltic source of most ancient amber.

Attempts to distinguish various kinds by other methods, for example, by a study

1. F. Hirth, *China and the Roman Orient*, 1885, pp. 41, 73, 245.
2. *Moralia* 2, 962 F.
3. iv. 202; πλεονάζει δε καὶ τὸ λιγγούριον παρ'άυτοῖς, ὅ τινες ἤλεκτρον προσαγορεύουσι
4. F. Schulten *Tartessos*, p. 65.
5. The fundamental articles are by O. Olshausen in *ZfE*, 1891, pp. 286–99 and O. Helm *id*, 1901, p. 400.

THE SUCCINIC ACID TEST

The following is a list of the ambers from Mediterranean sources which have been submitted to this test and the results published. (The methods employed in the test are described by Helm in *Zeitschrift für Ethnologie* 33, 1901, pp. 401–3. Helm shows that raw succinite contains 3–8% of succinic acid but points out that ancient examples if badly weathered lose some of their acid content and therefore a very low acid content is only proof of non-Baltic origin if the specimen was in a good state of preservation. In the following list of tested ambers the colour and condition of the amber is given where it is known).

Object	*Source*	*Condition*	*Result*	*Reference*
Beads	Mycenae, Shaft graves (Schliemann)	(*a*) very weathered skin	1·6% S.A.	*ZfE* 33, 1901
		(*b*) similar skin removed before testing	6% S.A.	H. Schliemann, *Tiryns*, London, 1886
Beads	Knossos, Tomb of Double Axes	not known	succinite	Evans, *P of M* ii, 174
Beads	Bologna, (Gozzadini excavations)	not known	4·8–6·3% S.A.	*ZfE* 33, 1901
Beads	In Pigorini Museum			*ZfE* 33, 1901
	(*a*) from Iesi (near Ancona)	golden translucent with red-brown patina	5·8% S.A.	
	(*b*) Palestrina	red-brown, v.weathered	4·1% S.A.	*ZfE* 33, 1901
	(*c*) Carpineto (near Ascoli Piceno)	red-brown, v.weathered	4·8% S.A.	*ZfE* 33, 1901
Beads	Vetulonia (Poggio alla Guardia)	red-brown, v.weathered	5·26% S.A.	*ZfE* 33, 1901
Beads	Novilara (near Pesaro)	Opaque, golden, v.thick patina	6·15% S.A.	*ZfE* 33, 1901
Beads	Kakovatos	not known	succinite	*AM* 34, 1909, p. 282
Bead	Castione (Parma)	not known	succinite	*ZfE* 23, 1891, p. 291
Beads	Ras Shamra	red-brown, light patina	probably Baltic	C. F. A. Schaeffer *Ugaritica* 1, 1939, p. 100
Beads	Pylos 1952 (Ano Englianos Tombs 89 & 94)	red-brown, opaque skin	positive for succinic acid	*BSA* 53/4, 1958/9, p. 261
Beads	Arvi (Crete)	red-brown, heavy patina	slight for succinic acid	*BSA* 53/4, 1958/9, p. 261
Beads	Thisbe Treasure, 1935	red-brown, heavy patina	positive for succinic acid	*BSA* 53/4, 1958/9, p. 261
Beads	Chios (Kato Phana)	red-brown	positive for succinic acid	*BSA* 53/4, 1958/9, p. 261
Beads	Capua (in Ashmolean Museum)	red-brown	negative	*BSA* 53/4, 1958/9, p. 261

of the organic remains enclosed in them, have not so far been convincing.[1] Another test, that of fluorescence under ultra-violet light, which depends upon the quantity of sulphur in the specimens, has not yet been carried out on a sufficiently large number of examples to judge its usefulness; however, it seems to be true that fluorescent Baltic amber is rare, whereas among the amber resins of Burma and Sicily it is common. It is very much to be hoped that modern scientific methods of analysis will provide positive and conclusive data to solve this problem. The possibilities of spectrographic analysis hold out some hope for the future.

IV. TRADE

The beginning of indirect trade between the northern amber-bearing regions and the Aegean falls in the late Bronze Age; amber appears first in the Shaft Graves of Mycenae. De Navarro[2] thought that the source of this amber was the West Jutland coast rather than the Baltic and that it came south by two well-worn routes (see fig. 1), one of which had already been traced by Montelius. The picture now is perhaps not quite so simple and it may be that some amber was also coming from the east Baltic in Bronze Age times by the eastern route which de Navarro believed was not opened until the Iron Age, or along the Danube to the Black Sea and Anatolia. But de Navarro's conclusions are still broadly acceptable. The nature of the prehistoric amber trade has emerged more clearly in recent years, but many problems still remain. There is no proof of any direct contact between the amber-bearing regions and the cities of Mycenaean Greece, but trading links between the Mycenaean world and central Europe are firmly established. The trade seems to have been conducted by middlemen on the route and the distribution of finds in Greece suggests that the amber was traded down the coast from the head of the Adriatic.[3] This trade continued throughout Mycenaean times.

There is no reason to believe that the trans-continental amber trade ended with the collapse of the Mycenaean world. The trade to the peripheral regions of the Classical world, especially to the north-west Balkan area, seems to have continued throughout the Mediterranean Dark Ages, and a good deal of amber has been found in sub-Apennine and proto-Villanovan contexts in Italy (see below, p. 24).[4] Only a trickle of amber seems to have reached Greece, though it was probably plentiful immediately to the north in Macedonia (see below, p. 22). The Greeks, therefore, and the Etruscans probably acquired their taste for the material from neighbouring tribes who had long been using it, but there is little doubt that the

1. V. Zanon, 'Le diatomee dell' ambra' in *SE* iii, 1929, pp. 427 ff.

2. *GJ* lxvi, 1925, pp. 481–507.

3. See below pp. 16 ff.

4. *NS*, 1960, p. 360 f.

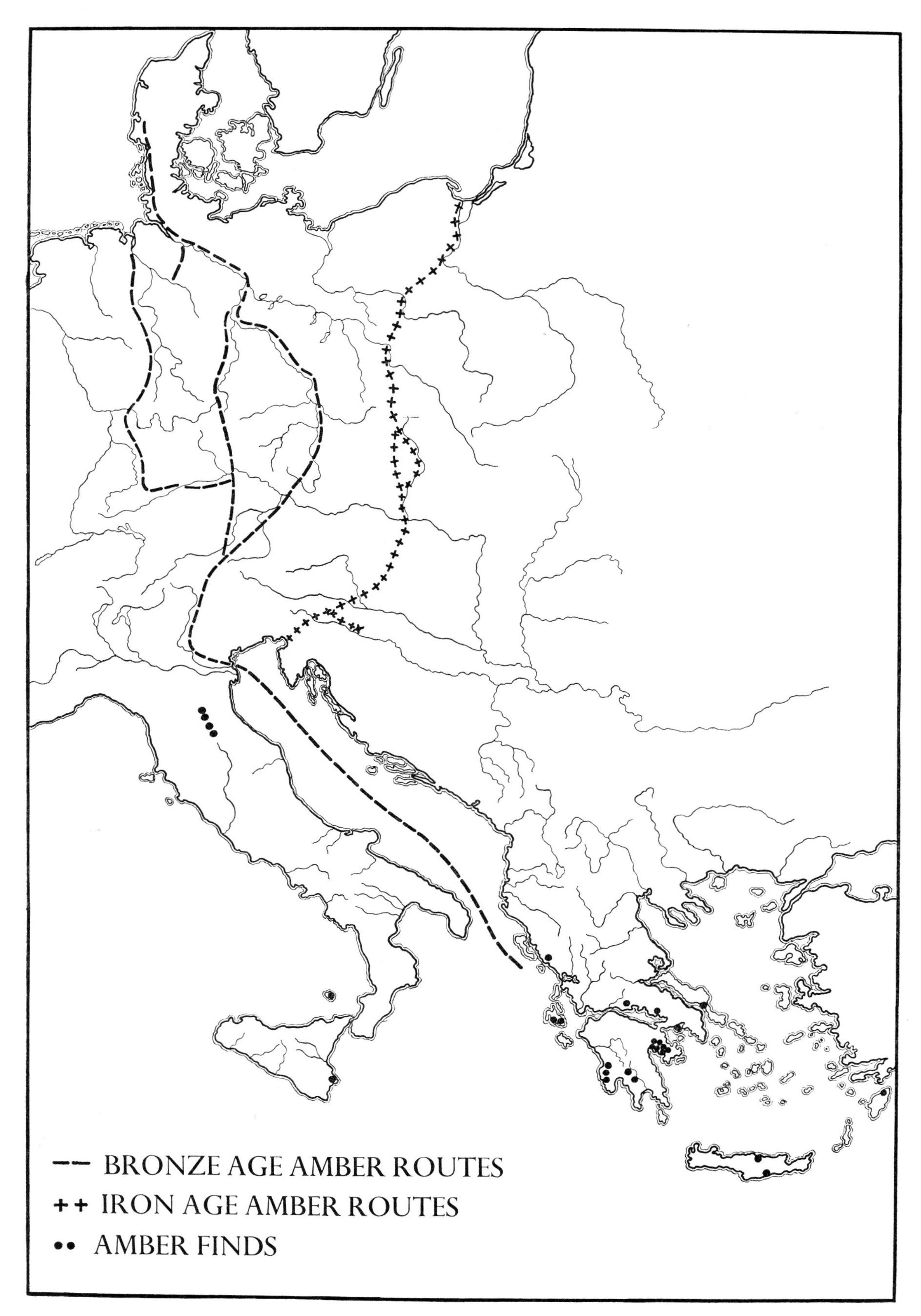

Fig. 1

northern amber trade took on a new vigour as a result of their interest. The Etruscans will have got their earliest amber from their neighbours in central Italy but soon began to trade further afield to obtain it. The Greek colonists in south Italy found the Iron Age tribes of the area using amber[1] but they also were able to tap other sources.

According to de Navarro, amber in the Iron Age reached the Mediterranean mainly from the east Baltic by a route coming down to the region of Trieste (fig. 1) whence it was shipped across the Adriatic to Italy. 'In this connection', he says, 'it should be noted that the eastern districts of that country, more particularly Picenum, are extraordinarily rich in amber finds'. Picenum may indeed have been the main area from which amber was distributed throughout the Italian peninsula. The Greeks may have traded for their amber either directly with the tribes of the Adriatic coast or with the Etruscans[2] and some of it probably came to them via Macedonia and Thrace. There is ample evidence for direct Greek trading up the Adriatic with the tribes of Illyria and the N.W. Balkan area; this trade flourished from the middle of the 7th century to the late 6th. From Macedonia amber could have passed by sea to the islands and E. Greece along the route of the mythical Hyperboreans.[3] It may also have been obtained from the Black Sea colonies.

In Greece amber was not used for decorative purposes after the sixth century and ceased to be imported in quantity, though some amber was always available. In Italy generally the taste for the material lasted well into the fifth century and in some areas down to the fourth. In Picenum it is rare after about 300 and only very few amber carvings have been found anywhere after that date until Roman times, although there are one or two amber earrings of second and first century date from Italy.[4] However, it may be assumed that small quantities of the material were always passing into the Mediterranean area. Fashion explains the decline of the trade. The Celtic invasions did not, in general, affect the amber trade which continued to the N.W. Balkan area down to Roman times.

Pliny's evidence suggests that amber became popular again in the early Empire but was not available in any quantity until the time of Nero, when the amber route from the Baltic had been explored by Roman enterprise as far as the Vistula.[5] The earliest Roman amber carvings represented by the series of little figurines of actors and grotesques (nos. **109–113**) which have been found at Pompeii and elsewhere seem to belong to the early first century A.D. and some may be as early

1. *MA* xxxi, 1926, p. 161 ff.
2. As suggested by Dunbabin (*Perachora* ii pp.522-3) and others.
3. Herodotus iv, 33.
4. E.g. a pair of gold earrings enclosing negro heads in amber from an Etrusco-Roman chamber tomb at Bettona in Umbria (*NS*, 1916, p. 15) for the type of earring see *Antiquité Vivante*, 1959, pp. 234–46 and Becatti, *Oreficerie*, pl. CVII.
5. *NH* xxxvii, 45.

as the later first century B.C. But the flourishing period for the use of amber in Roman Italy extended from the Flavians to the Antonines when Aquileia was the main centre of importation and manufacture. The Roman coins found in the Gulf of Danzig date mainly from A.D. 138–180 implying that this was the optimum period for Roman trade with the region.[1] On the route from Aquileia via Carnuntum–Opole–Kalisz–Osielsk, three hoards of amber making up a total quantity of 2750 kg, have been found, but they date, according to Majewski, from the first century B.C.[2] The direct trading links with the Baltic seem to have broken down in the third century A.D. It was probably the movements of the Goths that did most to kill the amber trade. Preidel notes that after A.D. 200 amber became much more common in Bohemian graves and this is presumably the corollary of the decline in dealings with the Mediterranean.[3] There do not in fact seem to be any carved ambers in Mediterranean regions much later than A.D. 200, but as late as the sixth century we hear of an embassy from the Baltic lands bringing a gift of amber to Theodoric.[4]

Bibliography

W. Helbig, 'Osservazioni sopra il commercio dell' ambra' in *Atti Lincei* (*Memorie*), 1877.

E. Sturms, 'Der ostbaltische Bernsteinhandel in der vorchristlichen Zeit' (in Jahrbuch des Balt. Forschungsinstituts, Commentationes Balticae I, 1953).

J. M. de Navarro, 'Prehistoric routes between N. Europe and Italy defined by the amber trade' in *GJ*, lxvi, 1925, pp. 481–507.

J. M. de Navarro, 'The British Isles and the beginning of the northern Early Bronze Age' in *The Early Cultures of N.W. Europe*, H. M. Chadwick Memorial Vol., 1950, pp. 77–105.

J. G. D. Clark, *Prehistoric Europe*, 1952.

N. K. Sandars, *Bronze Age Cultures in France*, 1957.

A. Spekke, *The ancient amber routes and the geographical discovery of the Eastern Baltic*, 1957.

A. B. Cook, *Zeus*, vol. ii, p. 493.

JHS, 1925, 229 ff.

J. R. Maréchal, 'Le commerce de l'ambre dans l'Antiquité' in *Techniques et civilisations*, vol. v, No. 4, 1956, 128–48.

V. THE USES OF AMBER IN ANCIENT TIMES

Among the peoples of Europe in the Bronze Age and Iron Age amber was always a much used and highly prized commodity. Several reasons contributed to its popularity. It is attractive in appearance, pleasant to the smell and the touch,

1. R. E. M. Wheeler, *Rome beyond the Imperial frontiers*, London, 1954, p. 23.
2. K. Majewski, *Importy Rzymski w Polsce*, Warsaw, 1960, p. 139; see also O. Brogan, 'Trade between the Roman Empire and Free Germans' in *JRS* xxvi, 1936, p. 201. For the route, Ptolemy (ed. Müller), i, p. 267.
3. H. Preidel, *Germanen in Böhmens Frühzeit*, Leipzig, 16 ff.; see also *JRGZM* 7, 1960, p. 228.
4. A. Spekke, 'Aistu sūtni pie Theodorika Ravennā' in *Veltījums prof. R. Viperam*, Riga, 1939.

and its magnetic properties[1] gave it a reputation for magical and amuletic virtues. It was also believed to have great medicinal value among primitive peoples. Pliny,[2] writing of the tribes beyond the Po, says 'hodieque Transpadanorum agrestibus feminis monilium vice sucina gestantibus, maxime decoris gratia, sed et medicinae; creditur quippe tonsillis resistere et faucium vitiis, vario genere aquarum iuxta Alpis infestante guttura hominum'. Even among the Greeks and Romans amber was generally considered to have medicinal qualities and was worn by children 'amuleti ratione'. Roman women often carried small lumps of amber in their hands during the summer because of its pleasant smell and its coolness to the touch.[3] Similar reasons, no doubt, induced the Emperor Elagabalus to pave a portico of his palace with pulverised amber.

The amber carvings of Iron Age Italy underline the magical aspects of the use of amber. Etruscan necklaces include a wide range of amulets of local and foreign derivation (see pp. 27–8), and the whole series of 'Italic' carvings consist largely of pendants worn in life as charms and in death with some apotropaic purpose. The big necklaces combined several well-known symbols of fertility, among them the ram's head, the frog and the cowrie shell. The *bulla* which is common in amber was one of the best known forms of amulet in ancient Italy. Many of the more enigmatic subjects among these carvings probably have a meaning that is no longer clear to us. Women seem to have been the chief users of amber in Etruria; although fibulae have been found in burials of both sexes, the necklaces were worn by women and children only. Among the Picenes amber was almost entirely confined to female burials and was used by the excavators as a clear indication of the sex of the deceased.

In early Greece the amuletic virtues of amber seem to have been generally recognised, a fact which may account for the survival of Minoan and Mycenaean amber into Archaic times (see pp. 21–2). Some of the early Greek animal carvings were probably amulets and an amber bead found in the Idaean Cave was made in imitation of north Syrian amulets. But in the Greek world generally the principal attraction of amber was its decorative qualities; it was used for fibulae and pins, for necklaces and for decorative inlays, especially in conjunction with ivory. It was not apparently put to any practical uses, although a passage in Aristophanes *Knights* 532 which refers to the use of amber in the manufacture of lyres, leaves it uncertain whether the use was decorative or whether some operative part of the instrument was made of the material.

In the Roman Empire amber again became a popular material especially for articles of adornment which were worn exclusively by women.[4] Amber rings and

1. These are mentioned by Plato *Timaeus* 80 C; τὰ θαυμαζόμενα ἠλέκτρων πέρι τῆς ἕλξεως
2. Pliny xxxvii, 44.
3. Martial v, 37, 11.
4. *NH* xxxvii, 30, 'Proximum locum in deliciis, feminarum tamen adhuc tantum, sucina optinent'.

necklaces were especially popular. One or two practical uses are referred to by ancient writers. Pliny mentions amber knives for cutting truffles—an idiotic affectation, no doubt—and refers to amber spindlewhorls in Syria.[1] Because amber is pleasant to the touch it was commonly used for handles of various implements.[2]

From about the middle of the first century A.D. the workshops of Aquileia began to turn out little decorative carvings in amber—bunches of fruit, animal figures and so on. The little carvings of corn ears and fruit were given as New Year presents and several have inscriptions referring to this; it seems clear that in this custom the magical properties of amber were still significant. At the same time amber began to be made into small pots for cosmetics and the like, and these were elaborately decorated with carvings. Large vases such as were to be found at the tables of the very wealthy[3] no longer survive, but their general appearance may be deduced from the miniature vases that have come down to us.

Apart from these carved utensils, amber was also in use purely as an art-material. We hear from Pausanias[4] of an amber portrait, perhaps a bust, of Augustus at Olympia, and Pliny mentions that the cost of a little amber figure of a man 'exceeds that of a healthy slave'.[5] Many of the small Roman amber carvings at Aquileia and elsewhere are of high quality, and it looks as though, for a brief time at least, amber attained much the same eminent position as a material for the production of objets d'art as it held in the sixteenth and seventeenth centuries.

Bibliography

Pauly-Wissowa sv Bernstein.

Blümner, *Technologie* ii, pp. 381 ff.

VI. ANCIENT TECHNIQUES OF AMBER CARVING

Amber is a comparatively soft and easily worked material which requires no special tools for carving it. However, a high proportion of natural amber contains faults and impurities which can make it useless for carving, and most of the larger pieces used in antiquity have some such faults, whose presence had either to be ignored or adapted by the sculptor to his design. Thus the deep cavities on the principal side of the group no. **35** are natural and the artist has arranged the figures so that they are least conspicuous. Apart from this disadvantage, amber,

1. *ibid.* 37.
2. E.g. the figured knife handles from Heerlen in Leyden (*Oudh Meded Leid NR* XI, 1930, p. 80 ff.) or the Etruscan sword handles (*MemAmAc* iii, 1919, pl. 24).
3. Juvenal *Sat.* v, 38; xiv, 307.
4. 5, 12, 5.
5. *NH* xxxvii, 49.

being a completely amorphous substance, is a most satisfactory raw material for sculpture because it is not liable to break up when carved and can be easily polished and drilled.

The earliest Mediterranean ambers, for example the beads of the Mycenaean period, were cut to shape and then given a final polishing with pumice or some similar substance. The few surviving Mycenaean engravings on amber show that the fine detail could already be worked on this material; the borings through the amber for stringing were presumably done with a small drill. In ancient, just as in modern amber carving, the detail is obtained by abrasion rather than by cutting. Modern amber workers have as their principal tools the file and various grades of emery paper; while their ancient counterparts used file and pumice. The final polish was imparted by means of powdered gypsum rubbed on with leather or the like.

The technique employed in the larger carved pieces of Italic workmanship may be studied on such examples as no. **36** in the Museum's collection. The craftsman accepted the shape of the natural amber lump and did no more than clean out the faults, one of which is a deep cavity going through the piece. He then proceeded by means of a small abrading tool to work the main outline of the figures in low relief. The last details, the hair and features, were carved with a small graving tool and are still hard and sharp in outline. None of these Italic ambers are deeply cut or drilled; the sculpture is always in low relief and so conditioned by the shape of the lump that features and limbs are often distorted into impossible attitudes. In no. **38** the long horizontal boring for suspension was apparently made after the relief was carved; it was bored from two sides so as to join in the middle and one end was damaged in the process. A curious and unexplained feature of a large number of these Italic ambers are the holes bored into the material and then stopped up with amber of a similar or different colour. These may be clearly seen, for example, on the back of no. **49** (pl. xxi).

The methods of carving amber in Roman times are clearly different from those employed in the Italian Iron Age. Figures on rings, small pyxides, etc., are carved in much higher relief and some are so deeply undercut as to be almost in the round (see no. **119**). In low relief work such as the satyr-head, no. **118**, the mouth is quite deeply carved; the drill was used to render the nostrils, and the features are much sharper and more precise in detail. The lathe was used to turn lids and bases of pyxides and for the manufacture of disc-components of such objects as the 'sceptres' in the Aquileia Museum and elsewhere. So far as we know, no use was made of the fact that when heated in linseed oil amber becomes soft and can be pressed or moulded; by this means opaque spots or other blemishes in the material can be made to disappear.

VII. THE COLOUR OF ANCIENT AMBER

It will be noted that almost all the ancient amber described in this catalogue is now red in colour, and as this is not the common natural colour of Baltic amber some explanation of the fact seems necessary. The natural colour in Baltic amber ranges from pale yellow to brown and it may be transparent or cloudy; the change in colour and the patination and cracking of the surface have taken place as a result of atmospheric weathering. Only in the mud of the Po valley which covers the site of ancient Spina has the original colouring and surface polish of a number of Italic ambers been completely preserved.[1] It may be worth while to quote at length the account of amber-colours given by Bauer, *Precious Stones*, London, 1904, p. 537. 'The colouring of amber is very uniform in character, no colour but yellow having been met with in a large quantity of Baltic amber hitherto collected. It varies in shade however from the palest yellow to dark yellow and brown. Material which has undergone a surface alteration is often red in colour but fresh specimens have never shown this colour. . . . One serious drawback to the use of amber is its tendency to change colour with the lapse of time. This change in colour is due to a chemical alteration which takes place gradually from without inwards. Pale-coloured specimens become darker and those which were brown become red or brownish red. The change is noticeable after a lapse of only a few years but differs in character in different varieties of amber. Clear amber becomes slightly darker and redder in colour and numerous cracks develop in its substance. In bastard amber an external layer becomes brown in colour and assumes a waxy lustre. Osseous amber acquires a porcelain-like lustre and in frothy amber an external layer sharply marked off from the remainder becomes quite clear and brittle.

'These alteration processes proceed gradually especially along cracks in the material until the whole mass has undergone the change. They were at one time attributed to the action of light but have since been observed to take place in the dark. When a piece of amber is kept in water or otherwise excluded from contact with the air, the change which takes place in it is much less in extent so that the process is simply a case of atmospheric weathering. . . . The external weathered layer is easily detectable from the nucleus of fresh unaltered material which is often pitted with close set shallow conical depressions. These affects of weathering are only to be seen in specimens which have lain in dry earth; those which have been embedded in perfectly dry sand being often changed and altered throughout their whole mass. Material, on the other hand, which has lain in water of moist earth, thus being preserved from contact with air, is often scarcely altered at all and does not show even the surface sculpturing described above.'

1. For these see below p. 29.

In the Bronze Age and the early Iron Age the clear varieties of amber were favoured and there seem to be very few cloudy pieces surviving. The Romans made much more use of the cloudy varieties. No attempt is made to assign modern names to the various kinds of amber represented in the collection but only to describe their present appearance; the vast majority of the pieces are now clear red in colour with surface cracking and sometimes severe pitting and patination. At Ephesus Hogarth[1] noted in the same deposit what he believed to be two different varieties, one a dusky red, cracked and patinated, and the other a clear tawny colour which had resisted the processes of disintegration and discoloration, but it seems much safer to assume that different soil conditions, even over a small area, had produced this result. Among surviving Roman ambers, a number of very fine pieces still preserve a clear tawny colour, notably some of the best animal carvings at Aquileia and Udine, and the opaque and mottled varieties were also much in demand for their decorative qualities. Pliny[2] says that a variety called Falernian, was the most highly prized. The following are the different colours observed in the large collection of Roman amber at Udine.

1. Translucent red; surface patinated and rough.
2. Translucent 'amber coloured' (tawny); varies from light to deep.
3. Opaque mottled orange-red.
4. Opaque mottled orange-yellow.
5. Opaque deep red.

The majority of the pieces are type 3.

We also know from Pliny that amber was artificially tinted in Roman times[3] though there do not seem to be surviving examples in which it is possible to trace any artificial colouring. Artificial effects were however obtained in a number of Bronze Age and Iron Age (Etruscan) ambers by filling holes bored through the material with artificial colouring matter (see under nos. **24–26**) and, as already mentioned, in several of the Italic figured ambers holes seem to have been filled up with amber plugs of a different or similar colour (e.g. nos. **46–50**). It looks as though some of the amber fibulae (e.g. no. **24*e***) combined segments of different natural colours.

1. Hogarth, *Ephesus*, pp. 213–4.
2. The passage *NH* xxxvii, 47, may be quoted here in full 'Genera eius plura sunt. Ex iis candida odoris praestantissimi; sed nec his nec cerinis pretium; fulvis maior autoritas; ex iis etiamnum amplior translucentibus praeterquam si nimio ardore flagrent; imaginem igneam in iis esse, non ignem placet. Summa laus Falernis a vini colore dictis, molli fulgore perspicius, in quibus et decocti mellis lenitas placeat'.
3. xxxvii, 48, 'Verum hoc quoque notum fieri oportet, quocumque modo ea tinguere libeat tingui haedorum salso et anchusae radice, quippe iam et conchylio inficiuntur', and *ibid*, 51.

VII. AMBER IN THE MEDITERRANEAN WORLD

I. THE BRONZE AGE

a. *Mainland Greece*. The earliest carved amber has been found in the LH I Shaft Graves of Mycenae.[1] Graves I, III, IV and V of Grave Circle A, among which there were both male and female burials, and grave omicron of Grave Circle B, all contained a large number of amber beads. The most prolific in amber was grave IV of Grave Circle A which contained 1290 beads; many globular and flattened disc-beads were found in it together with four or five flat rectangular 'spacer' beads described by Karo[2] as 'flachen, rechteckigen Platten . . . mit 5 durchlaufenden Fadenlöchern, offenbar zum Zusammenhalten von 5 Reihen kleiner Perlen'. A similar find was made in Grave Circle B (grave omicron) consisting of beads and three rectangular pieces with several borings through the amber.

Somewhat later in context than the Shaft Grave amber are the beads found in great quantity in the LH II A Tholos A at Kakovatos;[3] these consisted of disc beads generally of flattened biconical section together with a few beads of a more rounded shape and several flat pieces of amber with complex systems of through borings. The flat pieces were 'spacer-beads', rectangular or trapezoidal in form, which together with the other beads presumably made up necklaces of crescentic type.[4] The Kakovatos find also contains two ring-pendants and two flat pieces of amber in the shape of a figure-of-eight.

The spacer beads from the Shaft Graves and Kakovatos have provoked much controversy. The characteristic feature of these beads is the series of parallel through borings linked by V-borings at either end, a system which has also been found on beads from a number of Middle Bronze Age sites in Britain, South Germany and Alsace. It is generally believed that the Mycenaean examples were imported from Europe but as yet there is no general agreement as to their place of origin. Von Merhart argued[5] that the Mycenaean spacers came from South Germany where similar beads have been found in the Reinecke BI phase of the Tumulus culture, and he proposed to make use of the beads as evidence for dating phases of that culture. Werner[6] argued in favour of the British affinities of the Mycenaean beads and his view has recently been re-stated by Hachmann[7] and Marinatos.[8] Milojčić,[9] on the other hand, thought that the spacers from Grave Omicron were made in Greece and that some of the S. German beads might have been exported

1. Schliemann, *Mycenae and Tiryns*; Karo, *Schachtgräber*; G. Mylonas, *Ancient Mycenae*, Princeton, 1957.

2. Karo, *Schachtgräber*, p. 110, no. 513.

3. *AM* 34, 1909, p. 278 ff.

4. Similar beads were found very recently in a tholos tomb at Peristeria, near Pylos (*TO ΕΡΓΟΝ*, 1962, p. 110, *BCH* 87, 1963, p. 783 ff.).

5. *Germania*, 24, 1940, p. 99 ff.

6. *Atti del I Congresso internazionale di Preistoria e Protostoria*, Rome, 1950, p. 293 ff.

7. R. Hachmann, 'Bronzezeitlicher Bernsteinscheiber' in *Bayerische Vorgeschichtsblätter*, 22, 1957, p. 1 ff.

8. *BCH* 87, 1963, p. 787.

9. *Germania* 33, 1955, p. 316 ff.

from Greece. The chronological difficulties of linking the Mycenaean beads with the S. German examples seem insuperable.[1] In the case of Britain something like a closer chronological link between the spacers found on Wessex I and II sites and those of Mycenaean Greece seems possible, but direct trading connections between Greece and Britain in the sixteenth century have not yet been established and are perhaps unlikely. It is also true that although the spacers found in Britain and Greece are very similar, the forms of the ordinary beads are not very close to one another. On the whole it seems more likely that the beads came from Central Europe, from some centre which was closely linked with the central amber route, but so far there is not conclusive proof of where that centre might be.[2]

Although the earliest amber objects found in the Mycenaean world were probably imports, two of the Kakovatos ambers would seem to be of local manufacture; these are the figure-of-eight pieces of which another example has been found at Mycenae. Generally the use of the material was confined to beads. An amygdaloid seal from Tomb 518[3] at Mycenae (LH I/II) is engraved with the figure of a bull and a similar object was found in a tomb at Pellene in Laconia,[4] but these seem to be the only surviving Mycenaean attempts at more ambitious carving of the material.

Finds of amber beads of all the LH periods have been made in Greece. A tholos of about the same date as Kakovatos (LH II A) at Pylos (Epano Englianos) contained a large number,[5] and a necklace of 54 beads was found in an LH II tholos at Myrsinochorion (Rutsi) near Pylos. It has been suggested that there was some loss of popularity after LH I/II. At Mycenae, for example, tombs 515, 518, and 529 of LH I/II produced beads in considerable quantity but in the LH III tombs, nos. 517 and 526, there were only a few. Persson thought that at Dendra amber disappeared in LH III partly as a result of a change of fashion and partly because of a re-orientation in trade towards the south in the latter part of the LH period. He seems, in fact, to use the presence of amber as an argument for assigning one chamber tomb to LH II although it was certainly still in use in LH III.[6] At Prosymna, on the contrary, Blegen found amber beads in all LH periods, and it is difficult to detect any significant change in the popularity of the material; tomb XLIV, one of the earliest (LH I), had three beads and three discs, perhaps used as inlay, while tomb LI, one of the latest (LH III), had fourteen beads.[7]

The popularity of amber in the later phases of LH III seems, in fact, to have been greater than at any other time, the material being carved into a number of

1. Hachmann, *art. cit.*, p. 24.

2. For a balanced judgement of this problem see N. K. Sandars, *Bronze Age Cultures in France*, Cambridge, 1957, and *Antiquity* xxxiii, 1959, p. 292 f.

3. Wace, *Chamber Tombs*, p. 86.

4. *ADelt.* 10, 1926, Παράρτημα, p. 43.

5. *BSA* 53/4, 1958/9, p. 261.

6. Persson, *New Tombs*, pp. 58–9.

7. C. W. Blegen, *Prosymna*, Cambridge, 1937, p. 286 f.

characteristic bead-shapes which do not seem to occur in earlier finds. The flattened biconical bead which is represented in irregular shapes in the Shaft Graves assumes in LH III a very regular form with neat concave chamfers (e.g. no. **1***a*), and is found in conjunction with a type of long bead having a double-concave (knucklebone) section divided by a sharp ridge (eg. no. **1***b*). There are also a number of shapes intermediate between the flat biconical type and the long double concave (knucklebone) variety. All the various forms were found together in the Tiryns hoard, strung together on wheel ornaments composed of fine gold wire which have been thought of as imports from Central Europe.[1] Another find of similar beads, the long bead predominating, was made in a tholos of sub-Mycenaean date at Metaxata on Kephallenia[2] and finds of single beads have been made in many other places.[3] It seems that on the mainland of Greece amber was as popular, in the LH III C and sub-Mycenaean periods as at any other time, and that the importation of amber from Central Europe went on for some time after the breakdown of Mycenaean prosperity.

List of Amber Finds in Bronze Age Greece

1. Analepsis (between Kynouria and Lacedaimon).	*ΠΡΑΚΤΙΚΑ* 1954, p. 284.
2. Asine.	O Frödin and A. W. Persson, *Asine*, Stockholm 1938, pp. 276, 390.
3. Delphi.	*Fouilles de Delphes* v, p. 21, fig. 94.
4. Dendra (Mideia).	Persson, *Royal Tombs*, p. 90; *New Tombs*, pp. 57–8, 87, 147.
5. Kakovatos.	*AM* 33, 1908, p. 295 ff. and *id.* 34, 1909, p. 278 ff.
6. Kalbaki (Epirus).	*BSA* 53/4, 1958/9, p. 237.
7. Kephallenia, Metaxata.	*AE* 1933, pp. 76 ff., 1919, p. 116;
Kephallenia, Lekkithra.	*id.* 1932, p. 116.
8. Khalkis (Euboea).	*BSA* 47, 1952, p. 89.
9. Menidi.	H. G. Lolling, *Das Kuppelgrab bei Menidi*, 1880, pp. 22 and 27.
10. Mycenae, Chamber Tombs.	Wace, *Chamber Tombs*, pp. 58, 61, 62, 74, 86, 93, 105, 205.
Mycenae, Shaft Graves.	H. Schliemann, *Mycenae and Tiryns*, London, 1878, pp. 203, 245; Karo, *Schachtgräber*, pp. 37 f., 57, 69, 137, 180, 189, 198, 350.
11. Nauplia.	*ΑΘΗΝΑΙΟΝ* 8, 1879, p. 524.
12. Pellene (Laconia).	*ADelt* 10, 1926, Παράρτημα p. 43.
13. Prosymna.	C. W. Blegen, *Prosymna*, Cambridge, 1937, p. 286 f.
14. Pylos, Epano Englianos.	*AJA* 58, 1954, p. 27–32.
Pylos, Myrsinochorion (Rutsi).	*Antiquity* xxxi, 1957, pp. 97–100, *ILN* April 6th, 1957, 540.
Pylos, Peristeria.	*ΤΟ ΕΡΓΟΝ*, 1962, p. 115, *BCH* 87, 1963, p. 783 ff.
15. Salamis.	*AM* 35, 1910, pp. 30–1.
16. Thisbe (Boeotia).	*JHS* xlv, 1925, p. 2, fig. 1.
17. Tiryns Treasure.	*AM* lv, 1930, pp. 119 ff.
18. Vapheio Tomb.	*AE* 1898, 144.

1. S. Marinatos, 'Lausitzer Goldschmuck in Tiryns' in *ΘΕΩΡΙΑ*, *Festschrift für W-H. Schuchhardt*, 1960, p. 151.
2. *AE* 1933, pp. 92 ff.
3. See below under cat. no. **1**.

b. *Crete*. Amber is rare in Minoan Crete and has not been found in contexts certainly earlier than LM III. Some resinous fragments reported from the EM III tholos at Porti were said by Evans not to be amber[1]. But one cannot rule out the possibility that some amber reached the Aegean before the time of the Shaft Graves since it appears in the Treasure of Dorak[2] and was reported from Troy;[3] amber has also been found in Copper Age sites in eastern Anatolia (e.g. Alaca Hüyük). Miss Sandars[4] notes three finds of the material from Crete—a gold bound disc and two flat disc beads from the Tomb of the Double Axes of LM III,[5] some beads from a tomb at Arvi near Amira on the S.E. coast of Crete[6] tentatively dated LM I/II by Evans, and two beads from the cemetery on Upper Gypsades, Knossos, of LM III A–B date. Amber beads are also reported to have been found in late graves in the Kalyvia cemetery at Phaestos[7] and Marinatos mentions a single bead found in a LM III chamber tomb at Kydonia.

The gold bound bead from the Tomb of the Double Axes is unique in the Aegean World and provides a curious connection with finds of similar beads in the Bronze Age tumuli of Wessex.[8] Childe has argued that the Cretan bead is of British manufacture,[9] but the dotted decoration on the British beads from Manton and Normanton does not occur on the example from the Tomb of the Double Axes and the precise connection between them remains uncertain.[10]

It seems likely that all the amber found in Crete, with the possible exception of the gold bound bead from the Tomb of the Double Axes, was imported from the Mainland. None of this amber is as early as the material from the Shaft Graves at Mycenae and all the bead-types have been found in much larger quantities on the mainland. The beads from Arvi for example are biconical discs and long biconical beads. A few amber beads found in post-Minoan contexts in Crete, for example in the Dictaean Cave and Kissamo in W. Crete, may be Minoan survivals (see list, p. 23). Two beads from the Dictaean Cave have the same double-concave shape as beads from LH contexts in Greece. An amber spacer-bead set in a gold mount from one of the Khaniale Tekke tombs near Knossos is very probably a survival from the Bronze Age.[11]

1. S. Xanthoudides, *The Vaulted Tombs of Mesará*, London, 1924, p. 69; one is inclined to agree with Evans' distrust of the analysis (Mosso, *Origini*, p. 291–2).
2. *ILN*, Nov. 28, 1959, p. 754, *The Dawn of Civilisation*, London, 1960, pp. 168–9.
3. H. Schmidt, *Schliemann's Sammlung Trojanischer Altertümer*, p. 244, nos. 6117–8; from an uncertain context.
4. *BSA* 53/4, 1958/9, p. 238.
5. Evans, *The Tomb of the Double Axes* (*Archaeologia* lxv, 1914, pp. 42/3).
6. Evans, *P of M*, ii, p. 174; now in the Ashmolean Museum, Oxford.
7. *Rend. Linc.*, Series v, vol. xvi, 1907, 299; Marinatos in *ΘΕΩΡΙΑ*, *Festschrift für W.-H. Schuchhardt*, 1960, p. 151.
8. See *AJ* v, pp. 68–70, and S. Piggott, 'The Early Bronze Age in Wessex' in *PPS* 1938, p. 95.
9. V. G. Childe in *Festschrift für Otto Tschumi*, pp. 70 ff.
10. There is a similar gold bound disc with some dotted decoration in Munich; it has no provenience.
11. *BSA*, 49, 1954, p. 215 ff

c. *Rhodes and the Cyclades.* Finds of amber have been rare in the Cyclades. A pair of ring beads from Delos[1] appear to be of Mycenaean date (cf. Kakovatos) but no other examples are recorded. Rhodes has produced more. The British Museum collection contains a group of beads (no. **1**), six complete or almost complete and three fragments, most of which came out of a single tomb of LH III C date at Ialysos. These beads are of the same types as those found in LH contexts on the Greek mainland—the biconical disc bead with concave facets and the long double-concave bead. They seem to have belonged to necklaces of graded beads and were almost certainly imported from the mainland, from some centre of production which distributed these characteristic shapes over the Aegean area.

d. *Cyprus and the E. Mediterranean.* There have been several finds of amber in Cyprus but not all are of certain Mycenaean context. The amber from Tomb 27 at Enkomi is, however, certainly Mycenaean[2] as are the beads from the same site now in the British Museum (no. **2**). The British Museum amber comes from two tombs one of which is LC III A (tomb no. 67) and the other LC III A–B (tomb no. 66); two beads, one from each tomb, have the biconical disc shape, another is a long cylinder and the rest are nondescript oval and round beads. Mycenaean amber also seems to have found its way to the coasts of the eastern end of the Mediterranean. At Ras Shamra (Ugarit) amber beads have been found in association with other Mycenaean objects and are used by Schaeffer as one argument for a Mycenaean colony at Ugarit in the fourteenth and thirteenth centuries B.C.[3] Most of the beads illustrated by Schaeffer are of the long biconical type found in several late Mycenaean contexts in Greece and one or two seem to have the characteristic double concave profile of the beads from the Tiryns Treasure. Another amber find was made at Atchana; it is described as 'an amber ball bound together with gold' and it was found with a scarab of Rhamses VI.

e. *The West (Italy and Sicily).* Amber has been found in at least four of the Terremare sites in N. Italy at Montale, Casinalbo, Castione and Borgo S. Donnino.[4] Occupation of these sites ranges through the periods Terramare IA–IIB which correspond in the currently accepted chronology with the LH periods in Greece. Both at Montale and Castione amber was associated with lower levels; at Castione it was found 'sepolta nel strato infimo' and at Montale it came from the 'metà inferiore' of the mound. At Montale five beads were discovered, one of which is described at 'disco lenticulare di ambra perforato nel centro' and the others are 'elementi di collana di ambra a doppio cono tronco'; the latter, which are now

1. *BCH* 71–2, 1947–8, p. 220, no. 69 and pl. 38, 11 and 12; they come from the Foundation deposit near the Artemision.

2. See below (Cat. no. **2**).

3. C. F. A. Schaeffer, *Ugaritica* I, Paris, 1939, p. 100–1.

4. G. Säflund, *Le Terremare delle Provincie di Modena, Reggio Emilia, Parma, Piacenza,* Lund and Leipzig, 1939, pp. 38 40, 42, 97, 104 f.

in the Museo Pigorini, Rome, are very like the sharp edged disc beads found in LH II and later contexts in Greece. It looks as though the presence of amber in the Terremare sites is an occasional by-product of the Baltic trade with the Greek world. In fact, it is not impossible that the beads were imported from Greece, but it is more likely that they came from Central Europe, and they are almost certainly not local products.

Amber is recorded from a number of Bronze Age sites throughout the Italian peninsula, but nowhere in very large quantities. Beads have been found in a number of settlements of the Apennine Bronze Age, for example at Borgo Panigale and Toscanella Imolese. It seems to become more common in the later phases of this culture[1] and on sites which mark the transition between the use of bronze and iron (see below, p. 24). In Sicily the finds of amber have been larger and more significant. In a late Bronze Age burial at Plemmyrium, Syracuse, of the Siculan II period, there were found thirteen beads said to have formed part of a single necklace of about 140 beads in various materials.[2] The beads of amber, together with an ivory comb decorated with incised spiral ornament, seem to be Mycenaean imports; they include the characteristic flat biconical bead. Amber is also found at Castelluccio, especially in Siculan II, corresponding to the later phases of LH.[3] A large find of amber beads was made on the Piazza Monfalcone site on Lipari; the necropolis dates to the Ausonian II period whose earliest possible date is around 1150, but did not begin, according to some authorities until after 1000 B.C. It corresponds, broadly speaking, with sub-Mycenaean in Greece. The beads from Piazza Monfalcone[4] are identical with those used to adorn the gold-wire ornaments in the Tiryns Treasure—thin biconical beads with concave chamfers and larger double concave beads with dividing ridge. They underline the wide distribution of these characteristic LH and sub-Mycenaean shapes.

II. THE IRON AGE

a. *Greece.* De Navarro[5] was inclined to think that there was no break in the amber trade with the South between the end of the Middle Bronze Age and the beginning of the Early Iron Age, and it seems certain that large quantities of the raw material were reaching the periphery of the Classical world throughout the Mediterranean Dark Ages. Very little amber has, in fact, been found in the Greek world of a date between sub-Mycenaean (represented by the Tiryns Treasure) and the eighth century. Such ambers as the barrel head from the Dictaean Cave[6] and

1. *Civiltà del Ferro*, 513.
2. *NS* 1899, p. 31.
3. *BPI* xviii, 1892, p. 19; xxviii, 1902, p. 114; xxx, 1904, p. 253; xxxi, 1905, p. 121.
4. L. Bernabo Brea, *Meligunìs-Lipára, vol. I*, pp. 149–64, tav. XLIII; *ibid.* 'Necropoli ad incinerazione della Sicilia protostoriche' in *Civilta del Ferro*, Bologna, 1960.
5. *art. cit.*, p. 491.
6. Boardman, *Cretan Collection*, p. 73, no. 352.

the amber from the foundation-deposit near the Artemision on Delos are probably Mycenaean survivals; Desborough[1] believes that Kardiani Tomb I on Tenos is a burial earlier than 800, and this contained two amber beads and a fragment of a third which do not look particularly like Mycenaean beads. Finds from Early Iron Age tombs in Macedonia[2] near one of the main north-south routes across Europe date mainly from the eighth to the sixth century B.C. but the earliest graves in the Cemetery at Vergina in Macedonia have been dated as early as 1000 B.C. and one of these, a woman's grave, contained a necklace of amber beads.[3] Overland routes from the north must explain the considerable quantities of the material, often in rather rough state, found in Macedonia, but very little of it reached further south.

The material was not again used in any quantity in Greece itself until the Later Geometric period. One amber pendant was found in the Geometric deposit of Hera Akraia (late ninth–c. 750) at Perachora[4] and an amber figurine of a bird in Grave 56 of the Kerameikos.[5] It is in the later eighth and especially in the seventh century that amber was most popular in Iron Age Greece. Two hundred and twelve fragments of amber were found in the excavations of archaic Lindos on Rhodes. A fairly large find of amber dating to the Subgeometric and Orientalising periods was made at Aetos on Ithaca, forty-six pieces in all[6]; these included two small figurines of animals, a number of beads and a pin head. Finds of about the same date at Perachora, fifty-four pieces in all, included some intaglio seals.[7]

In this period amber was very extensively used as inlay in gold jewellery and ivory decorative work. Among the earliest examples of the former use are two earrings, one from the Isis tomb at Eleusis[8] and the other from the nearby Tomb A. The style of these earrings is strongly orientalising and it was, no doubt, of something of this kind that Homer was thinking when describing the necklace of the cunning Phoenician.[9] Some of the outstanding examples of inlay in ivory came from the sanctuary of Artemis Orthia at Sparta, mostly of seventh century date.[10] Artemis Orthia also produced a figurine of a recumbent sheep and the remains of a little intaglio. A very common use of amber at the period was as decoration of the bows of bronze fibulae in conjunction with ivory. Artemis Orthia and Perachora have both yielded numbers of such fibulae which are closely related to examples found in Southern Italy.[11] Throughout the seventh century amber

1. *Protogeometric Pottery*, Oxford, 1952, p. 159–60; *Ann.* viii–ix, 1925–6, p. 213.

2. E.g. Chauchitsa and Bohemitsa (*BSA* 26, 1923/5, pp. 7 & 9). There are beads of the same kind in the Stathatos Collection (P. Amandry, *Stathatos Coll.*, pl. 28, no. 191) and in the British Museum (Cat. no. **3**) from Chalcidice.

3. *Archaeology in Greece*, 1960–61, p. 18, fig. 18.

4. *Perachora* i, p. 77.

5. *Kerameikos* v, i, p. 197.

6. *BSA* 43, 1948, p. 117; of the Ithaca beads, some were as old as the third quarter of the eighth century (lower deposit) the rest were mostly seventh century.

7. *Perachora* ii, p. 523.

8. *AE* 1898, p. 103, pl. 6; the tombs date from the middle of the eighth century.

9. *Od.* xv, 459.

10. *Artemis Orthia*, p. 386; for the date of the amber see *BSA* 58, 1963, p. 7.

11. Blinkenberg, *Fibules* types XI, 9 & 10. See *Perachora* ii, pp. 523–525, where Dunbabin points out that though these particular types seem to be Greek, the idea is presumably Italic; see also *AJA* 62, 1958, 259 ff.

continued to be used for similar purposes. In the foundation deposit at Ephesus (c. 600 B.C.) amber, some of which is included in this catalogue (nos. **4–7**) was used for pin heads, inlays, beads and pendants. Of these the bulla-shaped pendants (no. **5**) are perhaps related to the pendants found in considerable quantities in Italy.

In the S. Italian Greek colonies amber serves much the same purpose as in mainland Greece. At Cumae some of the amber found may have been worked locally, some was probably imported ready-made from Etruria.[1] From Syracuse there are inlays[2] and many examples of the amber and ivory fibulae that are also characteristic of archaic sites in Greece. After about 600 B.C. the taste for amber seems to have shifted entirely to the peripheral regions of the Greek colonial area so that the archaic ambers of S. Italy as a whole, although heavily indebted to Greek art are better described as Italic than Greek (see below, pp. 24–33).

	Finds of Amber in Archaic Greece and Magna Graecia
Afrati, Crete.	*Ann.* x–xii, 1927/9, p. 477; *AJA* xlix, 1945, p. 315.
Athens, Kerameikos.	*Kerameikos* v, i, p. 197.
Centuripe.	*RM* xxiv, 1909, p. 97.
Chios.	*BSA* 35, 1934/5, p. 154; P. Jacobsthal, *Greek Pins*, 1956, p. 34.
Cumae.	*MA* xiii, 1903, pp. 265–7, figs. 45–6.
Cyrene.	*Africa Italiana* iv, 1931, p. 202, fig. 26.
Delos.	*Exploration archéologique de Delos* xviii, p. 309.
Dictaean Cave, Crete.	Boardman, *Cretan Collection*, no. 352.
Eleusis.	*AE* 1898, pp. 103, 107.
Ephesus.	Hogarth, *Ephesus*.
Fortetsa, Crete.	J. K. Brock, *Fortetsa* 1957, p. 54.
Ialysos, Rhodes.	*Clara Rhodos* iii, p. 118.
Idaean Cave, Crete.	Halbherr and Orsi, *Museo di Antichità Classica*, ii, p. 753 ff.
Ithaca (Aetos).	*BSA* 43, 1948, p. 117.
Kissamo, Crete.	Boardman, *Cretan Collection*, no. 422.
Knossos, Crete.	*BSA* 49, 1954, p. 216–17.
Lindos, Rhodes.	Chr. Blinkenberg, *Lindos* i, p. 110–1.
Megara Hyblaea.	P. Orsi, "Contributi alla storia della fibula greca" in *Opusc. Arch. Montelio dicata*, p. 194, fig. 3, p. 195 fig. 5*a*.
Olympia.	*Olympia* iv, p. 208.
Perachora.	*BSA* 43, 1948, p. 117; *Perachora* ii, pp. 523–5.
Pherai.	Blinkenberg, *Fibules* p. 201.
Praisos, Crete.	*BSA* 12, 1905–6, p. 64.
Samos.	*AM* 74, 1959, p. 27.
Siphnos.	*BSA* 44, 1949, p. 27, no. 7.
Sparta.	*Artemis Orthia*, p. 214–5.
Syracuse.	*NS* 1943, pp. 33 ff.; *NS* 1893, p. 457.
Thera.	*AM* 28, 1903, p. 238.

1. *MA* xiii, 1903, pp. 256–7, figs. 45–6.
2. E.g. the votive eyes of ivory and amber from excavations of the Athenaion (*MA* xxv, p. 599, fig. 198); another of these eyes was found at Chiusi (Montelius, pl. 218, 10).

b. *Italy*. The Iron Age peoples throughout the Italian peninsula carved an enormous amount of amber into beads and other objects of personal adornment. Among the Picenes of the east coast the material was so readily available that very large lumps were used to decorate the bows of bronze fibulae. Dall'Osso[1] refers to one such fibula as weighing a kilo and it is recorded that at Belmonte Piceno before any regular excavations took place the villagers used amber found in ancient tombs as fuel on their fires.[2] The same practice is recorded in the Perugia district.

Although amber is rare in Bronze Age Italy it becomes fairly common in the sub-Apennine and proto-Villanovan phases. Twenty-six beads of various kinds have been found in one proto-Villanovan burial at Poggio la Pozza near Allumiere and amber has been found on occupation sites of this and the preceding phase.[3] In the later phases of Benacci I at Bologna (corresponding with Archaic I in Etruria) amber is rather rare and is used only for beads; in Benacci II (corresponding with Archaic II or Early Orientalising period in Etruria) it is common. Throughout the seventh century in Etruria fibulae of various kinds, scarabs, small figure-pendants and inlays were made of this material. Early seventh-century graves at Veii contain many amber objects, those of the later seventh have very few, but outside Etruria the taste for the material lasts well into the fifth century B.C., the last stage of it being represented by the amber carvings which form the larger part of the collection in this catalogue (nos. **35–88**). Most of these belong to the later sixth and earlier fifth centuries B.C. and consist of relief carvings of animals, mythical and fantastic creatures, heads, figure-groups, etc. They are almost always pierced for suspension and were generally components of large necklaces; some served to decorate bronze fibulae. Amber of this kind has a wide distribution in Italy; the majority of examples come from S. Italy, especially Apulia, Lucania and Campania (see map fig. 2) but they have also been found in Etruria, Picenum and the northern parts of the peninsula. The centres of their manufacture are discussed below (p. 27ff.). Some may actually be the work of Greek craftsmen but the style of the majority contains more or less barbarous elements, and they were made to supply an essentially non-Greek demand for adornment. Examples of Italic amber carvings have been found outside Italy, for example at Novi Pazar in Serbia[4] in conjunction with late black-figured Greek vases. The latest examples probably date from c. 450 B.C. though they retain archaic elements of style which suggest an earlier period.

After the fifth century B.C. amber in Italy became much rarer. Some amber

1. *Guida Ancona*, p. xlii ff.
2. A. Bonarelli, 'Le ambre nelle tombe picene' in *Rend. Inst. Marchig.* 1927; *MA* xxxv, 1935, p. 409 ff.
3. *Mem Lincei*, ser. viii, vol. ix, 1959, p. 188; *Civiltà del Ferro*, 513.
4. In National Museum, Belgrade. The ambers from this place include a carved plaque with the figure of a warrior which seems to be of Greek workmanship.

was found in the cemetery of Montefortino (Marche) (? late fourth century) and there is an amber ring of the fourth century B.C. from Teano.[1] An Etrusco-Roman chamber tomb at Bettona in Umbria (second-first century B.C.) contained a pair of earrings with amber negro-heads enclosed in gold.[2] Some of the Hellenistic-Roman tombs at Ancona yielded amber of uncertain date[3] but it was not until the revival of the amber trade under the Romans that it became plentiful again.

Most of the amber described in this catalogue consists of carvings found in Italy, the two main groups being the collection of Sir William Temple which is said to come from Armento in the Basilicata[4] and those acquired by A. Castellani from the collection of Prince Sangiorgio Spinelli which are said to have been found at Canosa in Apulia.[5] Carvings in similar style belonging to the period 550–450 have been found in many other parts of the Italian peninsula. These late archaic and sub-archaic carvings from Italy, though they differ from one another in style and place of manufacture form a fairly well-defined group as regards their purpose and subject matter.

The distribution map of the principal published finds of ambers of this general kind shows (fig. 2) that they have been found over most of the Italian peninsula but predominantly in the south. The main types are as follows:

1. Head-pendants (*a*) frontal, (*b*) profile (e.g. nos. **44–60**).
2. Ram's head pendants (e.g. nos. **81–88**).
3. Pendants in the form of animals (e.g. nos. **63–80**).
4. Bullae, bottle pendants, etc. (e.g. nos. **89–91**).
5. Bullae, with figures or heads in relief (e.g. *MA* xxxv, 1935 pl. XXIX.)
6. Ring pendants (e.g. nos. **95–96**).
7. 'Cowrie shell' pendants (e.g. no. **94**).
8. Figure-groups in relief (e.g. nos. **35–40**); these may be pendants or parts of fibulae.

Scholars who have studied these Italic ambers have tended to think of one main centre (or at least, area) of manufacture such as Aquileia later became in the Roman period. There is much obvious truth in this view since, although several areas—Etruria, Picenum, Apulia—have their own distinctive varieties of beads and fibulae, the head-pendants, wherever they have been found and however much they may vary in quality, still form a fairly homogeneous group. Opinions have differed very considerably as to where the centre was. Helbig[6] discussing two amber groups in the Schwartz (later Stroganoff) collection argued that the Italic ambers

1. *MA* xx, 1910, p. 134.
2. *NS* 1916, p. 15.
3. *Guida Ancona*, p. 354 ff.
4. R. Gargiulo, *Catalogue of the Temple Collection* (Ms in the Greek and Roman Department). In the text of this catalogue references to Gargiulo's Catalogue are given in brackets after the registration number.
5. Detken, *Ambers*.
6. *BdI* 1877, pp. 13–14.

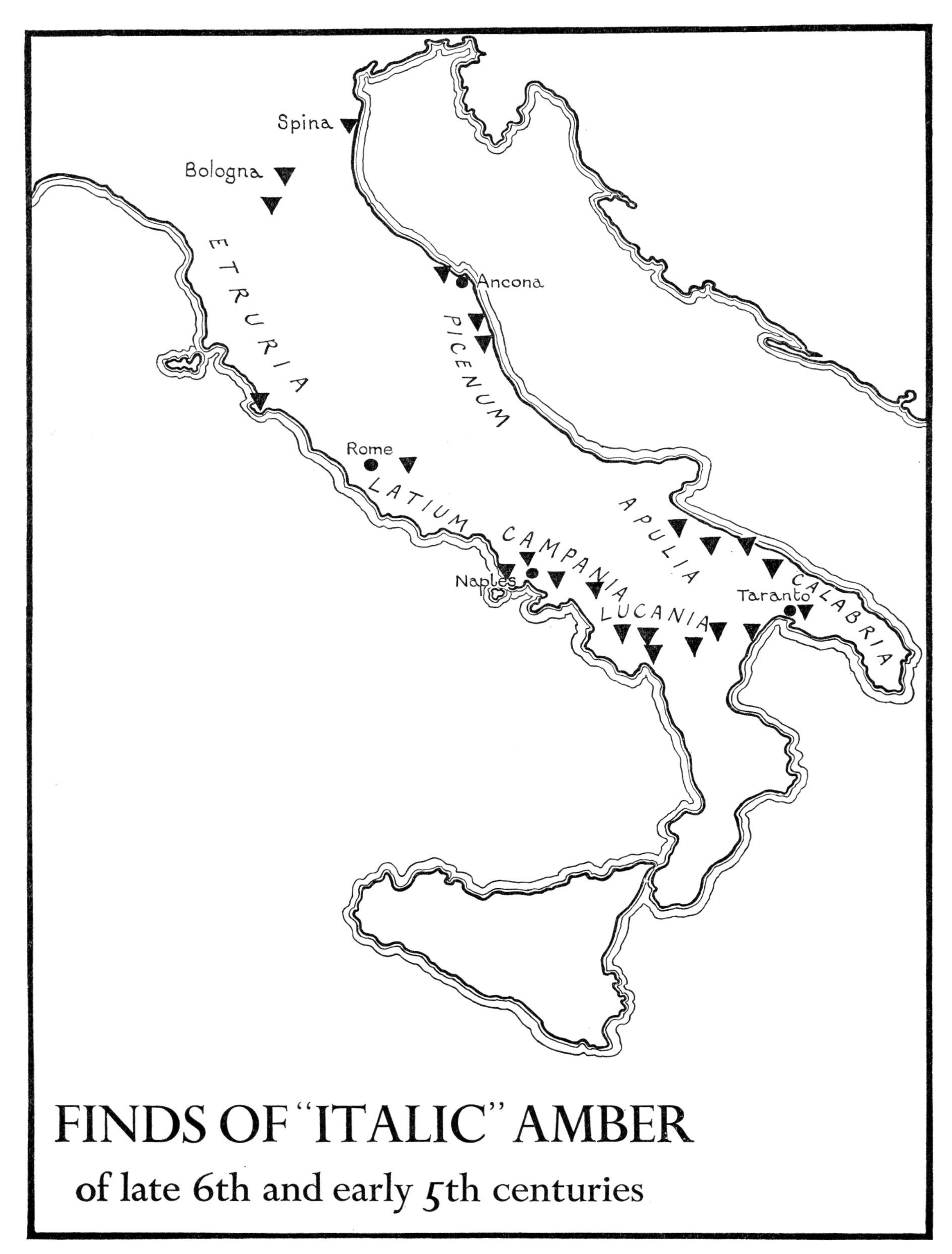
Spina
Bologna
ETRURIA
Ancona
PICENUM
Rome
LATIUM
CAMPANIA
Naples
APULIA
LUCANIA
Taranto
CALABRIA
FINDS OF "ITALIC" AMBER
of late 6th and early 5th centuries

Fig. 2

were 'Iapygian' work, partly on grounds of style ('un carattere piu o meno barbaro'), but mainly because in his time all the known examples seemed to come from the region of Bari, Canosa and Otranto. Pollak,[1] dealing with the same pieces somewhat later, rejected Helbig's hypothesis on the grounds that 'nous connaissons a present des pièces provenants des regions plus hautes de d'Italie comme, par example, de Picenum (Belmonte)'. He explained the barbarities of style in terms of the material and preferred to think of Picenum as the centre of manufacture. G. Pesce,[2] also seems to think that the only centre of production was Picenum and points out '. . . lavori piceni furono anche esportati in altre regioni d'Italia (se ne son trovati in Puglia e in Lucania), sulla costa dalmata . . .'. Miss Richter[3] is more cautious and contents herself with observing 'some claim them as Greek, others as Italic or Etruscan'. Albizzati held the view, mainly on stylistic grounds, that many of the Italic ambers were imported from Asia Minor and his view has been revived by Sestieri discussing a figure from Oliveto Citra[4] which he thinks came immediately from Sybaris and reached Italy from Asia Minor, perhaps Miletus. Of all the possibilities the Albizzati/Sestieri view is the only one that can be summarily ruled out; carvings of this class have never been found outside Italy and they belong to a period when amber was hardly used at all for decorative purposes in Greece (see p. 9). In assessing the problem here, we shall consider first the main areas where figured amber carvings have been found in Italy and follow with a brief discussion of their style. The main areas are:

1. *Etruria* (with its subsidiary, the Bolognese).
2. *Picenum.*
3. *S. Italy* (Campania, Lucania and Apulia).

1. *Etruria.* The use of amber in early Etruria is part of the Villanovan background of Etruscan culture. Amber was valued for its magical properties as it was in the rest of Iron Age Italy and many of the early Etruscan carvings are amulet-pendants of a strangely esoteric character that suggests primitive superstitions and beliefs. There is also a strong oriental, especially Egyptian, influence on the subjects chosen; apart from the scarabs we find Egyptian and Egyptianising deities represented among them.

Some of the earliest Etruscan amber carvings have been found at Vetulonia.[5] Apart from various kinds of beads and scarabs[6] the finds included necklaces with figure pendants in the form of humans and monkeys and there is one in the form of a frog. Monkey and figure pendants have also been found at Praeneste, at Marsiliana d'Albegna,[7] Falerii Veteres (Cività Castellana) and Narce in the

1. *Pièces de choix du collection Stroganoff.*
2. *Enciclopedia dell' Arte Classica* sv. ambra.
3. Richter, *Etruscan Collection*, pp. 31–32.
4. *Arch. Class.* iv. 1952, pp. 14–18.
5. Falchi, *Vetulonia*, pls. VII, VIII.
6. *SE* v, 1931, pp. 49 ff.
7. A. Minto, *Marsiliana d'Albegna*, 1931, p. 249.

Ager Faliscus.[1] Small figure carvings also served as decoration on the bows of fibulae. An unusual seal of oriental form with an intaglio of animals and men in primitive style was found in the Tomba del Tridente at Vetulonia.

Ambers in similar 'orientalising' style have been found outside Etruria in those areas which came under Etruscan influence. The finds from the Esquiline Necropolis[2] include a winged creature and a hare; a large and important group of carvings comes from Satricum in Latium[3] where the majority of the pieces are clearly local imitations of popular Etruscan types—monkeys and various kinds of grotesques including 'Januses' of human and animal form. Carvings of Etruscan type were popular among the Faliscans and have been found even further afield in the 'orientalising' phase of the Picene civilisation. A Janus-group related to examples from Latium was found at Castelbellino and a little figure of a monkey at Belmonte Piceno.[4]

After about 600 B.C. the popularity of amber in Etruria declined. Finds of the characteristic sixth century 'Italic' types have been rare in Etruria and Latium. Two heads from the Buffum Collection in the Museum of Fine Arts, Boston, are said to come from Palestrina and another similar one, also from Palestrina, is among the ambers in the Museo Gregoriano Etrusco. A female profile head pendant found at Populonia is a characteristic 'Italic' piece.[5] There are, however, one or two sixth century carvings which stand apart from the 'Italic' group and may well be purely Etruscan in workmanship. These include an amber statuette of a kouros from Orvieto, two little amber statuettes of women now in Dresden[6] and another very fine statuette of a woman in the Metropolitan Museum, New York.[7] There is no evidence to connect the 'Italic' group as a whole with Etruria.

In the Po Valley amber carvings with characteristic 'Italic' subjects are more common. A carving found in one of the Certosa tombs at Bologna represents a reclining animal backed by a sea-shell—a typically enigmatic subject—but most of the pieces, both there and at nearby Marzabotto,[8] are of rough workmanship, like the profile female head and the ram's head pendant from Tomb 100 on the Certosa site. A necklace from tomb 230 Giardini Margherita at Bologna[9] incorporates two roughly carved frontal human heads and a similar head was found in Certosa tomb 361. The profile head from Certosa tomb 350, though it shows some of the conventions of the general run of Italic ambers, has little in common with the better pieces in style. It seems likely that these pieces, most of

1. Dohan, *Tomb Groups*, pl. XVII (Narce Tomb 24M), G. M. A. Hanfmann, *Altetruskische Plastik* i, figs. 8*a* and *b*.
2. *MA* xv, 1905, pl. XIII, nos. 1, 2, 4, 5.
3. These ambers, which are not published, are on exhibition in the Villa Giulia Museum, Rome.
4. *MA* xxxv, 1935, p. 414, fig. 46 (right), *Guida Ancona*, p. 364 (right).
5. A. Minto, *Populonia*, p. 172, pl. XLIV.
6. Pelka, *Bernstein*, p. 28, abb. 12.
7. Richter, *Etruscan Collection*, figs. 104, 105.
8. G. Gozzadini, *Ulteriori scoperte*, pl. 15, nos. 16–25.
9. Unpublished.

which date from the late sixth century B.C., are of local workmanship imitating imported pieces. At all events none of them can compare in quality with the best 'Italic' ambers found elsewhere. Recent finds of amber from Spina at the mouth of the Po include three female profile heads, two from tomb 640 in Valle Pega and the third from tomb 514a, which are much closer to the style of the heads nos. **44–53** in the British Museum collection.[1]

2. *Picenum.* Picenum is probably the most prolific area in Italy for finds of ancient amber. As we have seen, de Navarro considers that it played the principal role in distributing the material over the Italian peninsula; after arriving in the region of Trieste, the amber would have been shipped down the Adriatic to Picenum. Some 'orientalising' amber carvings, related to those of Etruria have already been noted. Of the later pieces, four heads found at Vasto in 1912 are typical Italic profile head-pendants.[2] Many carved ambers were found in the cemeteries of Belmonte Piceno. They include a bulla with a Medusa head on one side and a series of little heads decorating the edge, a pendant with ram's head and dolphin on the edge, a double lion protome forming the bow of a fibula, two groups of a lion attacking a wild animal, all of which are typical 'Italic' pieces. The lion-groups and another lion pendant carved on a flat rectangular piece of amber are very similar in style to British Museum nos. **64–5**, **78** from Armento. The outstanding amber carving found in the Picene area is the group now in the Metropolitan Museum, New York, which is said to come from Falconara, north of Ancona.[3] It represents a woman and a youth reclining on a couch, perhaps Aphrodite and Adonis, and is one of the masterpieces of amber carving from Italy. Although raw amber was available in great quantity in Picenum, it seems unlikely that Picenum was the main centre for the production of 'Italic' ambers. The Falconara group, the lion groups, and the other examples of ambitious carving were probably imported, perhaps in exchange for the raw material.

3. *South Italy.* 'Italic' ambers have been found on many sites in Campania, Lucania and Apulia. The larger and finer pieces in the British Museum collection whose provenience is known come either from Apulia (Canosa, Ruvo) or Lucania (Armento). Other sites in the south which have yielded important pieces are Sala Consilina,[4] Padula,[5] Oliveto Citra[6] and Roscigno,[7] all in Lucania, and several sites in Apulia. A full list of published finds is given below (pp. 32–3).

Not all the ambers found in S. Italy belong to a single stylistic group. There are, for example, two quite distinct groups of heads among those found at Armento, of

1. *Mostra dell'Etruria padana* I, p. 371.
2. *Guida Ancona*, p. 361, top row; apparently lost, see *MA* xxxv, 1935, 425.
3. Richter, *Etruscan Collection*, p. 31, figs. 97, 98.
4. The Dutuit ambers now in the Petit Palais, Paris (cf. *NS* 1914, p. 406).
5. *NS* 1914, pp. 404–6.
6. *NS* 1952, p. 65; *Arch. Class.* iv, 1952, p. 14.
7. *Apollo, Bollettino dei Musei Provinciali del Salernitano* 1, 1961, p. 75 ff.

which one is carved in a flat archaic style characterised by large almond eyes, small nose and the hair in parallel lines (e.g. Cat. no. **46**) and the other in a more moulded three-dimensional style with the facial proportions more true to life (e.g. Cat. no. **54**). Heads in these two styles also seem to have been found together at Metapontum.[1]

The heads said to come from Canosa (Cat. nos. **44–45**, **47–53**) all belong to the first style and are mostly rather inferior to the ones from Armento. Heads in the style have been found over most of South Italy as well as Etruria, the Bolognese and Picenum. Heads of the second style seem to have a smaller distribution and all the recorded finds are from the southern part of the peninsula. We may therefore conclude, on the basis of distribution alone that the type 2 heads were manufactured in the south. It is also true that the best and largest examples of type 1 are from the south, and the widespread distribution of lesser quality pieces in the rest of Italy is best explained by export from S. Italy and by local imitations of imported types (e.g. pieces from Bologna and perhaps some of the pieces from Picenum). The very close connection between head-pendants from Roscigno in Lucania and those from Bologna and Spina suggests that many of the poorer quality heads were also made in the south and exported over Italy.

On the basis of these two types of heads, it is possible to distinguish two groups or styles among the more elaborate figured ambers from Italy. Related to type 1 is a group which may be called the 'group of the B.M. Satyr & Maenad' (no. **35**) and it includes:

1. The Satyr, no. **36**.
2. Two groups from the Stroganoff collection in the Louvre.
3. Fragment with female figure in Metropolitan Museum, N.Y. (Richter *Etruscan Collection* fig. 99, Pollak in *De Sanctis Mangelli Sale*, no. 232, pl. XI).
4. 'Atlas', no. **37**.
5. Female figure from Oliveto Citra.
6. 'Goddess', no. **39**.
7. Pendant with satyr head, Vatican no. 13474.

Another group, rather less compact, can be made up on the basis of the type 2 heads; the outstanding piece is the group from Falconara in New York. It includes:

1. Harpy pendants from Sala Consilina (Petit Palais).
2. Standing female figure, Metropolitan Museum, New York.
3. Warrior, Nat. Mus. Naples.
4. Lion group, Ancona.
5. Lion, no. **64**.

1. This provenience was given for a find on the London Market in 1953; its present whereabouts is unknown to me (photographs in the British Museum).

We may conclude that, in general, the amber carvings of the Italic class were made in the south and distributed over the peninsula. It is probable that some of the poorer pieces were made in Picenum and the Bolognese as imitations of the better S. Italian work, and it is likely that there were many centres in the south producing inferior work like the examples found at Roscigno and Metapontum. It remains to try to locate the centres where the finer pieces were made. The style of the carvings is very difficult to assess; it is very largely peculiar to the material but certain interesting stylistic comparisons are offered here as a small contribution to the problem.

A striking parallel for the female heads of type I with the hair confined in a head cloth and hair falling in deep waves on the forehead is provided by the figure of Auge on the top of a bronze dinos[1] in the British Museum; the details of the face, especially the eyes, are also very reminiscent of the ambers. The bronze is Campanian and its characteristic style has been discussed by P. J. Riis;[2] among the terracotta masks illustrated by Riis one may also mention as useful comparisons nos. A 3–4 (fig. 8)–cf. especially, the hair and headdress of nos. **56–59**.

A very close parallel for the slatted drapery on the B.M. satyr, no. **36**, is to be found on a pseudo-scarab in the Lewes House collection[3] which shows a bearded Dionysus; this, combined with the goggle-eyes and the forehead hair, to which Beazley draws attention, immediately argues a close stylistic connection with the whole group of S. Italian ambers. Other examples of such pseudo-scarabs, a number of which are in the British Museum (*BMC Gems*, nos. 453 ff) exhibit several of the same characteristic elements of style. Beazley is cautious over the Lewes House gem; he writes 'the style of the stone may perhaps be called Etruscan rather than Greek. If it is Etruscan, it is one of the earliest Etruscan gems'. I would prefer to think of them as S. Italian, very probably Campanian, especially the sard, B.M. 459 with a Siren on the scarab side and Apollo (?) on the flat. There is one in the Metropolitan Museum with a satyr-head on the scarab side and the Trojan Horse on the flat which is said to have been found at Populonia.[4]

If these analogies for the style of the Italic ambers are valid, it leads, I think, to the conclusion that the bulk of the better pieces were made under the strong influences of Campanian art of the sixth century B.C. Lucania, where many fine examples have been found, is the most likely centre but one cannot rule out the possibility of centres in Apulia where such fine pieces as the head from Roccanova, very close in style to no. **45** (from Canosa) have been found.

1. *BMC Bronzes*, no. 560.
2. 'Some Campanian types of heads' in *From the collections of the Ny Carlsberg Glyptotek* ii, 1938, p. 140 ff.
3. J. D. Beazley, *The Lewes House Collection*, pl. 8.
4. Richter, *Etruscan Collection*, p. 31, figs. 95–6.

Italic Amber: Museums and Proveniences

Museum	*Brief description*	*Provenience*
Munich, Antikensammlung	2 head-pendants	Italy
Vatican, Museo Etrusco	Pendant with a satyr torso; (*Rend. Pont. Accad.* vl, 131 fig. 4) fragmentary female figure; head-pendant, animal head.	
Bologna, Museo Civico	Many pieces—beads; pendants; ram's head pendants; animal group and miscellaneous	Bologna and Marzabotto
Paris, Louvre	2 figure groups from Stroganoff Collection; animal carvings; ram's head pendant	Italy
Paris, Cabinet des Médailles	2 heads (?)	
New York, Metropolitan Museum	See Richter *Etruscan Collection*, pp. 31/2	Italy
Naples, National Museum	i. warrior ii. ship relief and some unpublished pieces (e.g. Satyr, no. 113653 from Ruvo).	i. Ruvo ii. Padula
Paris, Petit Palais	pendants with harpy figures, animal carvings (*NS* 1896, p. 173; 1897, p. 166)	Sala Consilina
Stuttgart, Antikensammlung	2 head-pendants 2 ram's head pendants	Italy
Lyon	head-pendant	not known
Dresden, Albertinum	2 female figures (Pelka, *Bernstein*; *AA.* 1895 p. 227)	Italy
London Market	head-pendants, animals	Metapontum (photos in B.M.)
Taranto	head-pendant, bunch of grapes (*Ori e Argenti dell 'Italia Antica* nos. 318–9)	Roccanova
Ancona	head-pendants, animal carvings bullae etc.	Picenum
Ferrara	3 profile head-pendants (*Mostra dell 'Etruria padana* I, p. 371 nos. 1201–2)	Spina
not known	head-pendants, frontal and profile 'assai rozzamente scolpite' e.g. *MA* xxi, 1912, fig. 256	Cumae
Florence	head-pendant	Populonia
not known	female figure (*NS* 1952, p. 66)	Oliveto Citra
,,		Capua (*BdI* 1842, p. 37)
,,		Eboli (id)
,,		Anzi (id)

Museum	*Brief description*	*Provenience*
London, British Museum	various	Mainly Armento (Basilicata) and Canosa (Apulia)
Capua	tortoise, *BdI*, 1829, p. 187	
Bari	head-pendant	Bari
Boston, Museum of Fine Arts	2 satyr heads, male figure in relief etc.	Palestrina
Berlin	bottle-pendant with lion, harpy, satyr-heads, female head, ram	Lucania? and other places (obtained in Naples)
Gottingen	female head, two figure-groups	From Stroganoff Collection
Copenhagen, National Museum	heads and animals; 20 pieces	Abruzzi
Geneva	3 heads	not known
Schiller Collection (*Auction cat.* nr. 107, pl. 59)	sitting panther (attached to a necklace)	,,
Salerno, Museo Provinciale	many head-pendants, etc. (*Apollo* 1, 1961 pp. 75–88)	Roscigno

III. THE ROMAN PERIOD

The period when amber was most popular in the Roman world extends from the Flavians to the Antonines. This may be deduced not only from the finds of Roman objects in the east Baltic regions (see above, p. 10) but also from the finds made at Aquileia[1] which in the Roman period was the principal centre of manufacture of amber objects. The series of amber rings with female heads in the Aquileia Museum may be dated by the evidence of the coiffures to this general period and comparatively few pieces seem to come from the tombs of the third century A.D. One of the latest Aquileian tombs with amber is assigned to the end of second century A.D. The beginning of the period possibly coincides with the famous expedition of the *eques romanus*, sent by Julianus in Nero's time, who procured large supplies of amber and vastly encouraged trade with the Baltic regions.[2]

The earliest surviving Roman carvings are the group to which the figures, nos. **109** ff in the British Museum collection belong. Examples have been found at Pompeii[3] and some examples of this class may be a good deal earlier than the destruction of the city; a grotesque of this kind was found in a child's tomb near Rome dated to the time of Tiberius, the contents of which are in Berlin.[4] One example has been found at Aquileia but was probably not made there and differs in style from the majority of Aquileian ambers.

In the later first century A.D. Aquileia was the main centre which supplied the Roman demand for decorative amber carvings. It seems likely that the taste

1. G. Brusin, *Gli Scavi di Aquileia*, Udine, 1934.
2. Pliny, *NH* xxxvii, 45.
3. Siviero, nos. 561–9.
4. *JdI* 65–66, 1950–51, p. 279, figs. 2, 27; 5, 28.

for the material had never died in the northern parts of Italy and it is even possible that some legislation had to be made against its use in the late first century B.C.[1]

The Romans, while they seem to have accepted its amuletic virtues,[2] prized it mainly as an object of luxury endowed with high decorative qualities. Pliny the Elder, writing just before it became common, speaks of it as very valuable, and so, curiously enough, does Pausanias; however, the large quantities of carved amber surviving from Roman times suggest that only exceptionally large pieces were really very expensive. It was used principally by women whose taste is represented by several graves at Aquileia[3] and by the rich contents of a woman's grave at Vetralla.[4] Rings, small toilet vessels, mirrors, and various knick-knacks for ladies constitute the larger part of the Aquileian output. Two good examples of Aquileian work in this catalogue are the ring (no. **119**) and the little pot with its high relief decoration and beautifully turned base (no. **114**). Juvenal and Apuleius both refer to the use of amber for making drinking vessels; Juvenal[5] speaks of 'capaces Heliadum crustas' by which he must mean large vessels, and the most valuable of these, such as were to be found at the tables of the very wealthy[6], may have been made from single pieces of amber, but the majority must have been composed of small pieces. Some fragments found in Rouen are described as 'quelques débris d'un admirable vase d'ambre . . . d'assez grandes dimensions'[7], but, in the main we depend on the small toilet vases to give an idea of the larger pieces. Apart from these scent-bottles, etc. the Aquileian ambers include small decorative groups, animal sculptures, bunches of fruit and the like, some of which were purely ornamental while others served as mirror-backs[8] or lids for small pots. Various other toilet articles, among which one may perhaps include the little 'sceptres' made up of amber discs on a wire rod[9], were also made of amber.

Aquileian ambers were exported over a wide area of the Roman Empire, especially the north-western provinces. A large find was made in a tomb at Nîmes[10] and ambers from some tombs of the late second century A.D. in the Heerlen area are in the Leiden Museum.[11] Recently a handsome little amber group of Dionysos and a young satyr was found in a tomb in Esch in N. Brabant; the tomb dates from about A.D. 200.[12] In N. Italy Aquileian ambers are widespread, and they are

1. In the passage of Eusebius, *Hieronymi Chronicon* under the year 46 B.C. (A. Helm, *Die Chronik des Hieronymus*, 1956, p. 156) "Prohibitae lecticis margaritisque uti quae nec viros nec liberos haberent et minores essent annis XLV", the alternative reading for *lecticis* is *electris* but legislation against the use of amber is hard to understand in this period.

2. On the amuletic virtues if amber see S. Eitrem, *Opferritus und Voropfer der Griechen und Römern*, p. 194.

3. Brusin, *op. cit.*

4. R. Paribeni, *Il Museo Nazionale*, no. 1008.

5. Juvenal, *Sat.* v, 38.

6. Pliny refers to one weighing 13 lbs.

7. *Catalogue du Musée de Rouen*, 1875, p. 99.

8. *Ori e argenti*, nos. 422–423.

9. Brusin, *op. cit.*, fig. 128.

10. F. Mazauric, *Mem. de l'Acad. de Nîmes*, xxx, 1907, p. 300–2.

11. *Oud Meded Leiden*, *NR* xi, 1930, p. 8 ff.

12. *BABesch* xxxvii, 1962, 61 ff.

commonly found in Dalmatia.[1] Aquileian ambers from Sopron are now in the Kunsthistorisches Museum, Vienna and in the City Museum at Sopron; there have been large finds at Szombathely and elsewhere in the area. It is probable that amber was also being carved in a number of other Italian towns apart from Aquileia. A series of amber heads found at Ancona are probably of local manufacture; their date is uncertain but the style is related to a number of ivory and bone carvings of the Roman period.

Roman Amber: Museums and Proveniences

Museum	*Brief description or reference*	*Provenience*
Ancona	Several pieces (*Guida Ancona*)	Picenum
Aquileia	A large collection	Aquileia
Berlin (Staatliche Museen)	Several pieces including a heart shaped vase with vine leaves and fragment of handle with mask. (*JdI* 65–66 1950/1 p. 279, fig. 5)	Italy
Bonn	*BJ* 114–5, 1906, p. 362	Local
Brussels	*BJ* 114–5, 1906, p. 362	Local
Budapest, National Museum	Several pieces	Savaria
Budapest, Aquincum Museum	Several pieces	Aquincum
Cologne	*BJ* 114–5, 1906, p. 360 ff.	Cologne
Den Bosch, Central Noordbrabants Museum	*BABesch* xxxvii, 1962 p. 61 ff.	Esch (N. Brabant)
Dresden	A few pieces	not known
Este Museum	Objects from the collection of G. Capodaglio (*NS.* 1933, p. 389)	Aquileia
Florence, Pitti Palais	1 piece with Erotes	not known
Leningrad, Hermitage	2 statuettes, actors (?)	not known
Leyden	Several pieces (*Oud Meded Leiden* xi, 1930, p. 8 ff. figs. 7 ff.)	Heerlen
Munich	Relief of Eros on a vine leaf (*AA* 1929, p. 37)	not known
Naples	Several pieces (Siviero nos. 561–569)	Pompeii etc.
New York, Metropolitan Museum	Several pieces	not known
Nîmes, Maison Carŕee	Pyxis lid, animal sculptures	Nîmes
Obrovac	*ÖJh.* xii, 1909, Beiblatt pp. 96, 102	Starigrad (N. Dalmatia)
Paris, Louvre	Several pieces (de Ridder nos. 2118–2149 *bis*)	not known
Poetovio	Abramic, *Führer durch Poetovio*, p. 125, 87	Poetovio
Pollenzo	Ring with high relief decoration	Local
	Rings (Henkel, *Die römische Fingerringe* p. 150 ff.)	Rhineland (various sites)

1. Rostovtzeff, *SEHRE*, p. 567, note 35.

Museum	*Brief description*	*Provenience*
Rome, Museo delle Terme	Paribeni, *Il Museo Nazionale*, no. 1008	Vetralla
Sopron	Several pieces	Scarbantia
Szombathely	Several pieces	Savaria
Trier	several pieces	local
Trieste	*Aquileia chiama* 1, 4, 1954 72–4	Aquileia
Turin, Museo Archeologico	*Atti 7 Congresso di Arch., Class.* vol. ii, pp. 461–74	Libarna
Udine	*Aquileia Nostra* 22, 1951, 14–22	Aquileia
Vienna, Kunsthist. Museum	several pieces	Sopron and elsewhere
Vienna	'amulet'	local
Zadar (Zara)	Animal sculptures, baskets of fruit	Zara
not known	*Atti 7 Congress. di Arch. Class.* vol. ii, pp. 461–74; *AA* 1959, 115–20	Gravellona Toce
,,	*NS* 1880, p. 418	Concordia Sagittaria
,,	Ring with lion	Mologna (Bergamo)
,,	*Corriere della Sera*, 24. 10.59	Marcello (near Sesto Calende)
,,	*BdI.* 1860, p. 195	Volterra
,,	*BABesch* xxxvii, 1962, p. 65	Valkenburg (S. Holland)

CATALOGUE

NOTE: The word *provenience* is used in this catalogue to mean the place where an object was found; the word *source* is used for the immediate source from which it was acquired by the Museum.

MYCENAEAN

1. Beads

a. Flattened biconical bead
Diam. 2·5 cm., W. 1·2 cm. — [1]Reg. 72 3-15 40

b. Long double concave bead
L. 2·5 cm., W. 2·1 cm. — Reg. 72 3-15 41

c. Similar bead, smaller; broken
L. 1·9 cm., W. 1·5 cm. — Reg. 72 3-15 42

d. Long bead, facetted
L. 1·2 cm., W. ·7 cm. — Reg. 72 3-15 43

e. Two fragments of short barrel beads
W. (of largest) 1·2 cm. — Reg. 72 3-15 43

f. Short barrel bead, fragmentary
Diam. 1 cm., W. ·5 cm. — Reg. 72 3-15 43

g. Thin disc bead
Diam. 1 cm., W. ·2 cm. — Reg. 70 10-8 69

The amber is translucent red. *a* has a buff patina over its whole surface; *b* and *c* are lightly patinated and cracked on the surface; *d*, *e*, *f* and *g* have a deep brown patina over all. *b* and *c* were broken a long time ago, the cracked surface having a similar patina to the worked faces.

All these beads came from excavations at Ialysos on Rhodes. *a* and *b* (Furtwängler-Loeschke, *Mykenische Vasen* taf.B, nos. 12, 17) are said to come from Tomb 13 (*ibid*, p. 11); *c* which is like *b*, and similarly patinated, may be assumed to come from the same source. The pottery from this tomb is all LH III C. The provenience of the other fragments is not known, but all except *g* should come from tombs 13–18 which were discovered in 1871, their contents arriving in the Museum in 1872.

Most of the beads are characteristically late Mycenaean. Beads of types *a*, *b* and *c* have been found in conjunction in the Tiryns Hoard, where they served to decorate the spokes of gold wire wheel-ornaments (*AM* 55, 1930 p. 127; S. Marinatos, 'Lausitzer Goldschmuck in Tiryns' in *ΘΕΩΡΙΑ*, *Festschrift für W.-A. Schuchhardt*, 1960, p. 151). Single finds of type *a* beads include the tomb of Aigisthus of LH I/II (*BSA* 25, 1921–3 p. 304), a grave at Nauplia (*ΑΘΗΝΑΙΟΝ*, 8, 1879, p. 524) of LH

1. Under this number the Register of Antiquities lists 2 amber beads.

III(?), and a tomb at Upper Gypsades, Crete (*BSA* 53/4, 1958/9, p. 246). The largest find of type *b* beads comes from sub-Mycenaean tholoi at Metaxata on Kephallenia (*AE* 1933, pp. 76 ff.) and there are many similar beads from Ras Shamra (C. F. A. Schaeffer, *Ugaritica* I, 1939, p. 100). Other examples come from the so-called Thisbe Treasure (*JHS* 45, 1925, p. 2, fig. 1h), from a sub-Mycenaean grave at Salamis (*AM* 35, 1910, pp. 30–1) and from the Dictaean Cave (Boardman, *Cretan Collection*, p. 91, no. 352). In the West, the finds from Piazza Monfalcone on Lipari (L. Bernabò-Brea, *Meligunis* 1, p. 149, pl. XLIII) include many beads of types *a* and *b* and one of type *a* was found in a tomb (no. XLVIII) at Plemmyrium, Syracuse (*NS* 1899, p. 31).

2. Beads PLATE I

a. Flattened biconical bead
Diam. 1·8 cm. [1]Reg. 97 4-1 709

b. Similar bead, smaller
Diam. 1·4 cm. Reg. 97 4-1 301

c. Hollow cyclindrical bead, broken
L. (max.) 2·3 cm. Reg. 97 4-1 303

d. Oval plano-convex bead, pierced down its length
L. (max.) 2·3 cm. Reg. 97 4-1 300

e. Rectangular bead with rounded corners, flat on one side, humped on the other
L. 2·5 cm. Reg. 97 4-1 302

f. Thin disc bead
Diam. 1·1 cm. Reg. 97 4-1 304

Red translucent amber; the beads have deeply patinated surfaces, light or dark brown in colour and usually cracked and weathered.

These beads are all recorded in the Register of Antiquities as coming from two tombs at Enkomi; *a* is from Tomb 67, *b–f* are from Tomb 66. Amber beads from Tomb 66 are mentioned generally in *Excavations in Cyprus*, p. 43 and *b*, *d*, *e* and *f* are illustrated (pl. IX); *c* is mentioned specifically as 'a small amber cylinder, plain, broken and decayed'. *a* is not mentioned in the text of the volume nor is there any amber recorded from Tomb 67. Of the Enkomi tomb groups in the Cyprus Museum, only Tomb 27 seems to have had amber (J. L. Myres and M. Ohnefalsch-Richter, *A Catalogue of the Cyprus Museum*, p. 184). Tomb 66 may be dated LC III A–B and Tomb 67 LC III A. Beads *a* and *b* are very like the bead (Catalogue no. **1***a*) from Ialysos.

This amber is referred to in *BSA* 53/4, 1958/9, p. 239, where it is stated wrongly (note 55) that 'it was found not to be resin'.

ARCHAIC GREEK

3. Collection of rough amber beads PLATE I

Total length of beads as strung, 15·6 cm. Reg. 1933 6-14 22

Dark red translucent amber with very friable patination over the surface.

The beads are roughly shaped but the general form approximates to a biconical bead. They are said to have been found in Iron Age graves near Potidaea (*BMQ* vi, 1931/2, pp. 82/3; *ibid* viii, 1933/4, pp. 108/9). A large number of objects, including 78 amber beads of similar type, also from Chalcidice, are in the Stathatos Collection, Athens (P. Amandry, *Collection Hélène Stathatos*, Strassbourg, 1953, no. 191, pl. XXVIII). Ambers from Chauchitsa in Macedonia are mentioned in *BSA* 26, 1923–5, p. 24 and *Albania* 4, 42, 55, figs. 9 and 58 (see also Introduction, p. 22). Beads similar to these were found in graves of the seventh and sixth century at Trebenishte, (Filow, *Trebenischte*, p. 95, nos. 147–8, figs. 113–4, and *ÖJh* xxviii, 1933, p. 182/3).

The considerable quantity of Iron Age amber finds in N. Greece indicate a likely source from which the Greeks of the archaic period obtained the material. Purchased from J. Orfanidis in Athens.

4–7. Ambers from Ephesus PLATE II

These ambers all come from D. G. Hogarth's excavations at Ephesus on behalf of the British Museum (Hogarth, Ephesus*). The objects from the excavations were divided between the Archaeological Museum at Istanbul and the British Museum. A high proportion are from the Foundation Deposit of the Basis (for the date see P. Jacobsthal in* JHS *71, 1951, pp. 85–95 and 156–7). There is now no means of discovering from the Register of Antiquities exactly where an amber was found but with several of the entries there is a cross-reference to Hogarth's plates (i.e. a particular piece is described 'as pl.'). Ambers of all the types represented in the Museum were found on the Basis and the whole collection may be considered to be within the general dates for the Foundation Deposit.*

Hogarth classified the ambers as follows:

1. Embellishments of fibulae or other metal objects.

2. Suspensary ornaments.

3. Amulets.

4. Feminine ornaments, including pin heads, etc.

In classifying the material now in the Museum, this catalogue adopts the following arrangement:

4. Beads.
5. Pendants.
6. Pin heads.
7. Inlays on ivory astragali.

and this seems to cover the available material.

Hogarth distinguished (p. 214) two types of amber: (1) clear tawny of hard texture resisting disintegration; (2) more opaque and dusky red, friable, glowing deep crimson when held up to the light. At Kato Phana on Chios, Miss Lamb found ambers related to the Ephesian examples but distinguished only one type of amber which she thought was Hogarth's type 2 (BSA *35, 1934/5, p. 154). Among the Ephesus ambers now in the Museum, the clear tawny does not seem to be represented. All the amber is red and translucent; it may be more or less patinated and may vary in colour from deep crimson to light red. These variations are principally due to accidents of preservation and there seems no good reason to distinguish two fundamentally different types (for the colours and patina of amber in general see introduction pp. 14–15).*

4. Beads PLATE II

The beads shown in pl. II have been strung together in the Museum; the following are included (the classification follows Beck, *Beads and Pendants*).

a. Flat spacer with single lateral boring
L. 1·7 cm. Reg. 1907 12-1 504

b. Small disc
Diam. ·7 cm. Reg. 1907 12-1 505

c. Short cylinder
Diam. 1 cm. Reg. 1907 12-1 642

d. Standard truncated biconical
L. 1·2 cm. Reg. 1907 12-1 641

e. Short ribbed
Diam. 1·3 cm. Reg. 1907 12-1 501

f. Short oblate
Diam. 1·8 cm. Reg. 1907 12-1 499

g. Short oblate
Diam. 2·1 cm. Reg. 1907 12-1 ?

h. Short oblate
Diam. 2·7 cm. Reg. 1907 12-1 508

i. Short oblate
Diam. 3·3 cm. Reg. 1907 12-1 496

j. Standard truncated biconical
Diam. 2·7 cm. Reg. 1907 12-1 497

k. Short convex biconical
Diam. 2·3 cm. Reg. 1907 12-1 498

l. Short oblate
Diam. 1·6 cm. Reg. 1907 12-1 626

m. Standard biconical ribbed
L. 1·3 cm. Reg. 1907 12-1 502

n. Short oblate
Diam. 1·2 cm. Reg. 1907 12-1 500

o. Short barrel
Diam. ·6 cm. Reg. 1907 12-1 506

There are also two fragmentary beads from Ephesus in the Museum:

p. Cylindrical, transversely ribbed
L. 1·4 cm. Reg. 1907 12-1 643

q. Standard biconical
L. 1·1 cm. Reg. 1907 12-1 503

5. Pendants PLATE II

All the types in the collection are represented in the necklace on pl. II which has been strung together in the Museum.

Hogarth distinguishes these varieties:

a. 'Squat with a simple ring neck and no base, recalling a flattened aryballos or pilgrim bottle.'

b. 'elongated, with a gable-top and a pointed base, recalling a form of oenochoe.'

c. 'elongated, without base, but with round button-top, incised rosette pattern above'.

The flattish bulla-shaped pendant is the commonest form and corresponds to Hogarth's type *a.* The projection at the top is usually facetted and pierced for suspension. Often there is a ridge at the neck and the projection is occasionally grooved, perhaps to imitate a wire coil. Some of the pendants are more rounded, and others, like the large pendant in the centre, more elongated. One corresponds to Hogarth's type *b*, though it lacks the 'gable-top' of Hogarth's examples (*Ephesus*, pl. XLVII, nos. 18 and 27). There seems to be no example in the Museum of Hogarth's type *c*, of which the characteristic is the button-top with incised rosette pattern, though one or two with broken tops may have had this form.

The following pendants are included in the necklace (pl. II, from the right).

a.	Flat bulla-shaped (Hogarth type *a*)	Reg. 1907 12-1 534
b.	,, ,, ,, ,, ,,	Reg. 1907 12-1 533
c.	,, ,, ,, ,, ,,	Reg. 1907 12-1 532
d.	,, ,, ,, ,, ,,	Reg. 1907 21-1 520
e.	Elongated with pointed base (Hogarth type *b*)	Reg. 1907 12-1 509
f	Flat bulla-shaped, elongated	Reg. 1907 12-1 529
g.	Flat bulla-shaped	Reg. 1907 12-1 530
h.	,, ,, ,,	Reg. 1907 12-1 531
i.	,, ,, ,, elongated	Reg. 1907 12-1 535
j.	,, ,, ,,	Reg. 1907 12-1 523
k.	,, ,, ,,	Reg. 1907 12-1 522

The following pendants, not illustrated, are also in the Museum:

l.	Bulla-shaped, rounded	Reg. 1907 12-1 518
m.	Bulla-shaped, flat, neck broken	Reg. 1907 12-1 526
n.	Bulla-shaped, elongated	Reg. 1907 12-1 517
o.	Bulla-shaped, flat	Reg. 1907 12-1 521
p.	Bulla-shaped, elongated	Reg. 1907 12-1 536
q.	Bulla-shaped, flat	Reg. 1907 12-1 527
r.	Bulla-shaped, elongated, neck broken	Reg. 1907 12-1 538
s.	Bulla-shaped, rounded, neck broken	Reg. 1907 12-1 519
t.	Bulla-shaped	Reg. 1907 12-1 524
u.	Bulla-shaped	Reg. 1907 12-1 525
v.	Bulla-shaped, elongated	Reg. 1907 12-1 537
w.	Bulla-shaped, with collar	Reg. 1907 12-1 528

6. Pin-heads

PLATE II

The globular pin-heads with rosette finial are illustrated on pl. II. They vary in shape and size and one of them has a neck. These pin-heads were combined with pins of various materials. The Register of Antiquities refers to two on ivory pins (1907 12-1 540-1); this is the type illustrated by Hogarth, *Ephesus* pl. XLVIII, but, although there are several ivory pins of this kind in the Museum, none of them now has the amber in position. The biconical pin-head (pl. II*h*) is illustrated in Hogarth, pl. XLVIII, 25. Amber pin-heads were also found at Kato Phana, Chios (*BSA* 35, 1934–5, p. 154).

The following pin-heads are now in the collection:

a.	Globular with rosette finial	Reg. 1907 12-1 512
b.	,, ,, ,, ,,	Reg. 1907 12-1 511
c.	,, ,, ,, ,, and neck below	Reg. 1907 12-1 510
d.	,, ,, ,, ,,	Reg. 1907 12-1 514
e.	,, ,, ,, ,,	Reg. 1907 12-1 515
f.	,, ,, ,, ,,	Reg. 1907 12-1 513
g.	Globular, rather flattened	Reg. 1907 12-1 516
h.	Biconical	Reg. 1907 12-1 541

7. Astragali PLATE II

Three of the ivory *astragali* are illustrated on pl. II. The inlay always appears on one side only. On one side of each 'bobbin' is a round recess filled with an amber disc; this recess may almost fill the end or it may be quite small and serve as the central motif of an engraved design. The visible surface of the amber is either flat or convex. The single disc with amber inlay *q*, though not properly an *astragalus*, is catalogued with them.

The following *astragali* with amber remaining are now in the Museum:

a.	Plain rims, large convex discs of amber (2 preserved) L. 3 cm.	Reg. 1907 12-1 432
b.	Plain rims, large convex discs of amber (1 preserved) L. 2·5 cm.	Reg. 1907 12-1 435
c.	Plain rims, large flat discs of amber (2 preserved) L. 2·5 cm.	Reg. 1907 12-1 437
d.	Plain rims, large convex discs of amber (2 preserved) L. 2·6 cm.	Reg. 1907 12-1 434
e.	Plain rims, large flat discs of amber (2 preserved) L. 2·7 cm.	Reg. 1907 12-1 436
f.	Plain rims, large convex discs of amber (2 preserved) L. 2·6 cm.	Reg. 1907 12-1 438
g.	Plain rims, large flat discs of amber (1 preserved) L. 2·2 cm.	Reg. 1907 12-1 440
h.	Plain rims, 1 flat, 1 convex disc of amber L. 2·5 cm.	Reg. 1907 12-1 439
i.	Plain rims, with palmettes at junction, flat discs of amber (2 preserved) L. 2·6 cm.	Reg. 1907 12-1 441
j.	Plain rims, with palmettes at junction, flat discs of amber (2 preserved) L. 2·2 cm.	Reg. 1907 12-1 443

k. Plain rims with 1 flat, 1 convex disc of amber
L. 1·9 cm. Reg. 1907 12-1 445

l. Plain rims with convex discs of amber (2 preserved)
L. 1·9 cm. Reg. 1907 12-1 446

m. Engraved pattern on rim and small eyes (1 preserved)
L. 2·5 cm. Reg. 1907 12-1 453

n. Engraved pattern on rim and small eyes (2 preserved)
L. 2·7 cm. Reg. 1907 12-1 455

o. Engraved pattern on rim and small eyes (1 preserved)
L. 2·3 cm. Reg. 1907 12-1 458

p. Rim with engraved concentric circles and leaf at junction, flat discs (1 preserved)
L. 2·8 cm. Reg. 1907 12-1 447

q. Single disc with plain rim and flat disc of amber
Diam. 1·2 cm. Reg. 1907 12-1 465

8. Bead PLATE II

Diam. 1·7 cm.; thickness 1·2 cm. Reg. 86 4-1 1717

Orange-red opaque amber, very like the material of nos. **120** and **122.**

The bead was presented by the Egypt Exploration Fund and comes from Naukratis. It seems to be the only piece of amber recorded as having been found there; amber is rare in Egypt (cf. A. Lucas, *Ancient Egyptian Materials and Industries*, p. 444); there are a few scarabs of uncertain date, including one in the British Museum (H. R. Hall, *Scarabs*, p. 12).

9. Pendant PLATE II

H. 1·8 cm. Reg. 1919 11-19 14

Red translucent amber with deep browny-yellow patina over whole surface.

The pendant is neatly carved with a narrow neck and a thin collar. The neck is bored across for suspension, and a second boring runs diagonally downwards from the shoulder on one side. A break on one side of the neck is an old one, its surface having a heavy patina.

This amber was found with other objects of glass, electrum and gold together with a *cothon* with black decoration in a tomb one and a quarter miles S.E. of Aivasil near Lake Langaza in Macedonia. The *cothon* can be dated to the late sixth century B.C. (*BSA* 23, 1918/19, p. 17 ff.; *Perachora* ii, p. 525).

Presented by the British Salonica Force.

10. Bronze fibula with segments of bone and amber on the bow PLATE II

L. 7·5 cm. Reg. WT 1049 (*BMC Bronzes* 2078)

Deep red translucent amber with surface patina.

Bronze fibula with a flattish bow and a long catch-plate. On the bow there are two conical segments of bone at either end and a wide central segment of amber which was set flat on the bow. Further segments seem to be missing. The underside of the amber segment is flat and the top curved; there are three bore-holes through the amber, two of which are joined together.

The fibula was bequeathed by Sir William Temple and probably comes from S. Italy. The type seems to have originated in the Greek colonies of S. Italy, under the influence, perhaps of the segmental fibulae of central Italy. The general type is Blinkenberg XI, 9 (*Fibules*, 201–4). Very similar fibulae from the Fusco Necropolis at Syracuse were found with a Protocorinthian aryballos of the early seventh century B.C. (*NS* 1895, p. 122 & 148, fig. 30, see also *AJA* 62, 1958, pp. 259–272,) Other examples from Megara Hyblaea (*MA* xxxi, 1926, 344–5), Cumae (*MA* xiii 1903, p. 267, fig. 46) all of seventh century B.C. date. The same type of fibula has also been found in Greece at Perachora (*Perachora* ii, 439, where it is discussed by Dunbabin) and Sparta (*Artemis Orthia*, pl. LXXXII); for the relations between these fibulae and those of Central Italy, see *AJA* 62, 1958, pp. 272.

11. Bronze fibula with amber on the bow PLATE II

L. (of fibula) 10·8 cm. (of amber segment, 2·3 cm.) Reg. WT 816 (*BMC Bronzes* 2077)

The fibula had a flat elliptical bow and a long catch-plate, now missing.

The amber was threaded on to the central part of the bow; the surviving piece is plano-convex in section with shallow flutings on its convex side and three borings through its length, the central one to take the bronze bow. The decoration of the bow was probably completed with conical segments of bone like no. **10**.

Bequeathed by Sir William Temple; said to come from Torre Annunziata.

ETRUSCAN

12. Silver and amber pendant PLATE III

L. (of setting) 3·2 cm., H. 2·8 cm. Reg. 72 6-4 1006

Red translucent amber, flecked with golden tints of surface oxidation. The pendant consists of an oval piece of amber in a thin silver setting which swivels on an elliptical hoop with a wire tube at the top for suspension. The amber is held in the setting by a flange and by two claws of thin wire ending in double spirals. The tapering ends of the hoop pass through the setting into a boring through the amber. The piece of amber itself is flat on one side and convex on the other. The convex side is engraved with transverse grooves and ridges and fine hatching; the flat side is plain. Most of the flat surface is, in fact, broken away, revealing the series of thin borings through the length of the amber.

The pendant is Etruscan of the middle of the seventh century B.C. An example from a fossa grave of the mid-seventh century B.C. at Veii was found with a chain of silver wire from which it perhaps hung, and there were two human figures engraved on the flat side of the amber (*NS* 1954, p. 2). A similar pendant in gold was found at Vulci (Becatti, *Oreficerie*, no. 258b) and one of amber and silver in a grave at Cumae (no. XLIV) which also contained a Protocorinthian aryballos of the mid-seventh (*MA* xxii, 1913, p. 250, fig. 89). We may also compare the oval pendants of amber and gold making up a necklace in the Regolini–Galassi tomb at Caere (Pareti, pl. V; Becatti, *Oreficerie*, pl. LII). There are also four small amber scaraboid pendants in gold settings in the British Museum (*BMCJ* nos. 1465–8); one of these (no. 1468) is carved in the form of a scarab, and there seems to be some intaglio work on the flat.[1] The engraving on the convex side of the amber is similar to that found on amber scaraboids from various tombs at Vetulonia, Veii (see *SE* v, pp. 49–69), and from Narce (Dohan, *Tomb Groups*, pl. XXI, Tomb 23M). A scaraboid with hatched ornament on the convex side and a quadruped engraved on the flat was found recently in a fosse grave at Veii (*NS* 1963, p. 222). The series of borings like those on Etruscan fibulae, seem to be decorative. The same kind of mounting and swivelling hoop, usually in silver, is also used for scarabs of Egyptian type (cf. Montelius, Series B, pl. 192, 12).

1. I have decided not to re-catalogue these pieces here, nor the necklace with an amber bottle-pendant (*BMCJ* no. 1452; see also under no. **104**).

This pendant, with no. **13**, was bought from Alessandro Castellani who obtained it from the collection of Prince Sangiorgio Spinelli (Detken, *Ambers*, pl. IX A). According to Detken's catalogue all the Sangiorgio ambers came from a tomb at Canosa but there is strong reason to suspect this, especially in the case of these pieces.

13. Silver and amber pendant PLATE III

L. (of setting) 5 cm., W. 4·5 cm. 72 6–4 1007

Deep red opaque amber with surface cracking but almost no patina.

This pendant comes from the same source as no. **12** and is illustrated in Detken, pl. IX, where it is shown with most of the hoop and one of the leaf-shaped claws (cf. no. **14**) still in position. The hoop never seems to have been in the Museum and at present only the amber and the setting with the stump of the hoop survive. The amber is much more finely worked on the convex side than no. **12**; there is a broad convex band down the middle flanked by hatching.

14. Silver and amber pendant PLATE III

L. (of setting) 5 cm., W. 4·5 cm. No Registration no.

Red translucent amber with golden tints of surface oxidation.

The pendant is similar to nos. **12** and **13**, but larger. The setting is fixed by means of leaf-shaped claws soldered to the frame. The piece of amber is plano-convex like nos. **12** and **13**, and decorated very much like no. **13**. A convex band running across the middle is flanked on both sides by zig-zag hatching.

The pendant was also bought from Alessandro Castellani but is not one of the Sangiorgio pieces in Detken. Castellani said it came from Cumae which is a likely provenience; a similar one from a grave there, found together with a Protocorinthian aryballos of about 650, has already been mentioned (see no. **12**).

15. Scaraboid (included in a collection of glass and faience beads) PLATE III

L. 3 cm., W (max.) 2·3 cm. Reg. WT 1335

Dark red translucent amber, with heavy brown patina on one side.

The piece is badly cracked and broken. There are three parallel borings in the length of the amber of which only two go completely through.

The scaraboid is of the same type as that contained in the silver pendants (nos. **12–14**). On the convex side there is a central ridge flanked on either side by grooves and hatching.

Bequeathed by Sir William Temple; no provenience.

16. Necklace of amber pendants and gold beads PLATE IV

Total length, 29·5 cm. (approx.) [2]Reg. 72 6-4 719

The amber varies in colour from light to very dark red with dull and cracked surfaces.

The pendants are triangular in shape with a horizontal tube for suspension at the top. They are graded in size and vary from 2 to 2·5 cm. in length. On one side the pendants are flat and on the other they have three facets; there is a thin flat edge between the facetted side and the flat surface. There are fifteen pendants in all, most of which have been restored, and sixteen gold beads with a filigree frame round the openings.

Amber pendants of this shape are used in a necklace from Palestrina in Boston in combination with spirally hatched long beads and anchor-like pendants. Other triangular pendants of similar form have been found in a tomb at Narce (Dohan, *Tomb Groups*, pl. XXI, nos. 54-58 (Narce, tomb 23M) of the second half of the seventh century B.C.

This necklace, together with necklaces nos. **17–23** and the fibulae (nos. **24–27**), was purchased from Alessandro Castellani. These objects all come from Praeneste (Palestrina) mainly from two tombs, (1) on the Via Labicana ('about a mile before it falls into the Via Prenestina'), and (2) on a site behind the church of S. Rocco (excavated by Pier Luigi Galassi).

The contents of the tombs, which are published in *Archaeologia* xli, passed into the hands of Augusto Castellani who was a goldsmith. Amber objects were found in both the tombs and there is very little doubt that Castellani when he composed the necklaces, etc. catalogued here used components from both tombs. However the parts of nos. **16**, **17**, **18**, **19**, **21**, and **22** are substantially from the Labicana Tomb while the monkey pendant used in no. **23** probably comes from the S. Rocco tomb. In the case of the fibulae (nos. **23–26**) there are probably bits from both tombs but the gold leaf with hatched ornament is specifically referred to as coming from the S. Rocco tomb.

This necklace is illustrated in *Archaeologia* xli, p. XIII, 2 and in Pinza, *Materiali* Tav. 26 from water-colours by Alfredo Castellani; see also *AdI* 1866, p. 189, figs. G and H, *Monumenti* viii, pl. XXVI and Montelius, Series B, pl. 365.

17. Necklace of glass and amber beads and silvered bronze pendants PLATE IV

L. (as strung) 30 cm. (approx.) Reg. 72 6-4 622

Red translucent amber with light surface patination.

The principal feature of this necklace are the twelve silvered bronze pendants in the form of thin circular discs embossed with a dotted pattern of 7-point stars.

2. This object has the number 619 in the Castellani Register.

These discs have been much restored and backed with paper. The ten amber beads are ribbed short beads of a form that is known in seventh century contexts in central Italy, as for example in the Esquiline Necropolis in Rome (Gjerstad, *Early Rome*, ii, p. 253); they vary in size and quality. The glass beads are of various colours—yellow, black and white, and blue.

Part of this necklace is illustrated in *Archaeologia* xli, pl. 8, fig. 4, where it is said to come from the Tomb on the Via Labicana.

18. Necklace of faience and amber beads with silvered bronze pendants PLATE V

L. (as strung) 30 cm. Reg. 72 6-4 621

Red translucent amber.

The necklace consists of five spirally fluted and one plain long bead of amber, fourteen short ribbed beads of blue-green faience, three circular and four segmental pendants of thin silvered bronze with embossed ornament.

Long biconical beads, plain or hatched in some way, are common in seventh century contexts in central Italy, for example, Bisenzio, in conjunction with gold pendants (*NS* 1928, p. 437, fig. 5), and Vulci Tomb 22 (Dohan, *Tomb Groups*, pl. XLVIII). In a recently discovered, and not yet published, fossa grave on the edge of the Quattro Fontanili cemetery at Veii this type of bead was combined with rectangular spacer beads having three transverse borings. Similar finds were made in the Vaccareccia cemetery at Veii. The reliefs on the pendants are characteristic of Italic repoussé relief of the orientalising period. For similar faience beads, *MA* xv, 1905, tav. XII.

The pendants are from the tomb on the Via Labicana (*Archaeologia* xli, pl. 12, fig. 2, where they are illustrated without the amber beads).

19. Necklace of silver pendants and amber beads PLATE VI

L. (as strung) 61 cm. Reg. 72 6-4 1004

The amber of the beads varies in surface colour and condition of preservation; most of them are dark red in colour and heavily patinated.

The necklace consists of eighteen silver pendants in the shape of long-necked flasks with pointed bases, with tubes attached at the top through which the string is threaded. The pendants are divided from one another by amber beads, of which there are seventeen in all. These beads are of various shapes; there are five flat disc beads and the others are more rounded. It is possible that the flat disc beads are the original ones and the others replace beads missing when the object was found. There seems little doubt that the alternation of amber bead and silver pendant is original. A necklace of very similar pendants was found in the Regolini-Galassi Tomb (Pareti, pl. XIV) at Caere.

This necklace is illustrated in Pinza, *Materiali*, fig. 297.

20. Necklace of amber and glass beads PLATE VII

L. (as strung) 68 cm. (approx.) Reg. 72 6-4 718 (618 in Castellani Register)

The amber is red translucent, with light patina and cracking on the surface.

The necklace consists of 54 square beads of bi-pyramidal section separated from one another by little yellow and blue glass beads and a few amber beads. The square beads are graded in size, and the central feature of the necklace is a long bead of pointed oval shape from either end of which hangs one glass bead, one of the bi-pyramidal beads and one long spirally fluted bead (cf. no. **18**). In the Castellani Register this necklace is combined with silver pendants (*BMC Jewellery* 1357*); they have since been detached and are not mentioned by Marshall as belonging.

The bi-pyramidal type of amber bead is very common in seventh century contexts both in Latium and Etruria. There are examples from Capua (Tomb XCIV) Falerii Veteres, Vulci, Satricum, the Esquiline Necropolis (*MA* xv, 1905, pl. XIII) and Narce (Tomb 23M). A necklace from Palestrina in Boston is composed of different sized beads of this type, the larger alternating with the smaller.

Part of this necklace is illustrated in *Archaeologia* xli, pl. VII, fig. 2.

21. Necklace of amber pendants and glass beads PLATE VIII

L. (as strung) 12·7 cm. Reg. 72 6-4 1008

Red translucent amber, cracked and dull; the central bulla is very heavily patinated and deeply cracked.

Short length of a necklace consisting of seven amber pendants divided from one another by little beads of blue and yellow glass-paste. The amber pendants vary in size and type. Four are neatly turned pear-shaped pendants with a flanged neck and round attachment at the top which is pierced horizontally for suspension. Two are rougher and pear-shaped, one with a conical and the other with a rounded attachment above a slight neck. The type of pendant is very common in seventh century contexts in Central Italy (Dohan, *Tomb Groups*, Narce 19M, 7F). A very similar pendant from a fossa grave at Veii is illustrated in *NS* 1963, p. 240 fig. 107. The central bulla is very like nos. **90–1** and is probably an addition made by Castellani. In *Archaeologia* xli, pl. XIII, fig. 3 the bulla is not shown.

Said to come from the tomb on the Via Labicana.

22. Necklace of glass and amber beads and amber and faience pendants PLATE VIII

L. (as strung) 28 cm. Reg. 72 6-4 625

The amber of the beads is light red and translucent with cracked and dull surface; a number of the pendants have a deep orange-yellow patina.

The necklace consists of eleven amber pendants and eighteen small amber beads together with blue, black and yellow glass beads. The pendants are of two kinds; (1) of rounded shape with carefully worked neck and (2) of pointed oval shape, narrowing towards a facetted attachment at the top. Of these (1) is very common on Faliscan sites, e.g. Narce (Dohan, *Tomb Groups*, pl. XX) and (2) is frequently found on sites in Latium (e.g. *MA* xv, 1905, pl. XIII). There are six faience pendants, representing Ptah-Seker (cf. the pendants from Tomb C in the Esquiline Necropolis, Gjerstad, *Early Rome* ii, fig. 224).

One of the faience pendants is illustrated on a necklace (*Archaeologia* xli, pl. VIII, 5) which is referred to as coming from the tomb on the Via Labicana.

23. Necklace of amber and silver pendants PLATE IX

L. (as strung) 31 cm. Reg. 72 6-4 620

The amber of the beads varies in colour from light to dark red; the surface is shattered and dull.

The necklace consists of six straight-necked bottle pendants of silver, three similar pendants of amber and thirteen biconical long beads of amber, one of which has a badly patinated amber pendant glued onto it. The two largest and best preserved of the amber beads have flanges at both ends. The amber pendants seem to imitate the silver ones; the wire tube on top of the silver pendants, by which they are suspended, is imitated by grooving on top in two of the amber examples. The pendant in the centre of the necklace is an amber monkey, elbows on knees, holding his head in his hands. The amber bottle pendants are bored upwards from the base as far as the suspension tube and the monkey is similarly bored at least as far as the neck.

This necklace was recomposed by Castellani from objects found at Praeneste. In *Archaeologia* xli ape-pendants are referred to as having been found in the S. Rocco Tomb, but it is uncertain where the other pieces come from. Similar monkey pendants have been found in the Circolo dei Monili (Falchi, *Vetulonia*, pl. VII, *SE* xvii, 1943 pp. 31–42) and Circolo del Tridente at Vetulonia, (*NS* 1898, p. 93 and 1908, p. 437) at Narce (*MA* iv, 1894, p. 383), Veii (*NS* 1963, p. 240) and among the many amber pieces from Satricum in the Villa Giulia Museum there are monkey figures that seem to be copied from Etruscan pendants of this type. (For monkeys in Etruria see *SE* vi, 1932, 341 ff.) The bottle pendants and long beads of this necklace represent the best amber carving in S. Etruria and Latium. Similar beads and pendants have been found on many sites in this area—Bisenzio (Olmo Bello), Falerii Veteres, Satricum—and also in the Bolognese and Picenum. They all date from the seventh century B.C.

24–27. Fibulae with amber segments on a bronze bow PLATES X–XII

All the fibulae of this type in the collection were bought from A. Castellani and all of them, when a provenience is given, are said to come from Praeneste. They may be divided into four groups which are catalogued here under different numbers.

24. *Segments of amber only forming a boat-shaped bow usually slightly trapezoidal in plan. The degree of angularity in the centre segments varies. There may be three or five segments, and the fibulae must have been completed with end segments of a perishable material.* (**28**. *is a fibula of similar shape but composed of a single long segment of amber, a closely related type.*)

25. *Segments of amber combined with wooden(?) segments covered with gold leaf. The wood in these examples at present is in every case modern restoration but the leaf is ancient. There are usually three amber and two gold segments.*

26. *Amber segments forming a bow which is trapezoidal (kite-shaped) in plan. Probably a developed form of* **24** *and the two forms shade off into one another. Five to seven segments.*

27. *The bow is shaped like* **26** *but the segments are channelled transversely.*

The fibulae are nearly all modern reconstructions by Augusto Castellani, who certainly made use of segments that did not originally belong together. When this fact is obvious from patina or scale it is stated in the list that follows; where the bow or a fragment of it survives it is of bronze and it may be assumed that this was so in all cases.

These four variants of the same type of fibula ('a sanguisuga') are common in Villanovan and Etruscan contexts of the seventh century B.C. *The earliest examples, of Benacci I in the Bolognese* (Civiltà del Ferro, *p. 616) and Archaic II in Etruria* (NS *1882, 277, Tav.II 4) usually have short catch plates; the later examples favour a long catch plate. The various types are discussed in Sundwall, pp. 190 ff. The gold and amber fibula (no.* **25**) *seems to be confined to Etruscan and Latian sites; one of the largest and best preserved examples was found at Bisenzio (Capodimonte Tomb XII,* NS *1928, 457). Other examples from Palestrina are in the Museum of Fine Arts, Boston. A large number of fibulae with the amber segments preserved but the alternate segments of some perishable material now missing were found recently in excavations at Veii (Quattro Fontanili),* NS *1963 e.g. p. 240, fig. 107. The types composed entirely of amber segments are very widespread on Villanovan, Etruscan, Faliscan and Latian sites. Types* **26** *and* **27** *are the most developed in form (Sundwall, p. 190 ff); very close parallels for both these types have been found at Satricum (now in the Villa Giulia Museum, Rome). The amber segments of these fibulae (especially in nos.* **24** *and* **25**) *often have many smaller borings surrounding the central bore-hole through which the bronze bow passes; these are presumably for decoration like the complex borings in Bronze Age spacer beads, and may once have been filled with other substances. The Central Italian segmental fibula is obviously related to the Greek types (see under no.* **10**) *and may have inspired them; Etruscan examples reached S. Italy and Greece and are found in Central Europe (e.g. the example from Hallstatt, K. Kromer,* Das Gräberfeld von Hallstatt, *Florence, 1959, Grave no. 678).*

24. PLATE X

a. L. 2·9 cm., W (max.) 2·4 cm. [1]Reg. 72 6-4 1011

Five segments. The central segment is too large for its present position. The surface of the segments retains a polish; the colour is a deep translucent red, the texture shattered.

b. L. 3·7 cm., W (max.) 2·7 cm. Reg. 72 6-4 738

Five segments. The middle and end segments are badly pitted, the intermediate segments smooth and lighter in colour. They do not seem to belong together. Some restoration in plaster. Remains of a bronze bow in position at one end.

c. L. 2·5 cm., W. 2·0 cm. Reg. 72 6-4 663 [739]

Five segments. The amber (except that of one of the end segments which probably does not belong) still retains a surface polish. The texture is like *a*.

d. L. 2·5 cm., W. 2·1 cm. [2]Reg. 72 6-4 663 [739]

Three segments. The segments are a fairly good fit but the colour of the centre segment (opaque red) is quite different from the other two (polished red translucent). The central segment has several borings, the others have a single boring centrally. They did not belong together.

e. L. 2·2 cm., W. 1·8 cm. Reg. 72 6-4 663 [739]

Three segments. The segments fit well and the boring corresponds in each segment. The amber is red, translucent, shattered and dulled on the surface; the middle segment is darker than the others and may always have been so. Amber of different shades was probably often combined in these fibulae.

f. L. 2·9 cm., W. 2·5 cm. Reg. 72 6-4 738

Three segments. Amber dull on the surface, very little patina. One segment certainly does not belong; perhaps none of them were originally together.

g. L. 2·1 cm., W. 1·7 cm. Reg. number broken away

Three segments. Did not originally belong together; amber as above with rather rougher surface.

h. L. 1·8 cm., W. 1·4 cm. Reg. 72 6-4 663 [739]

Three segments. Did not originally belong together. Amber as above, with a good deal of surface pitting.

1. Under this registration the Castellani Register says, 'tre frammenti di fibula di ambra'; see also **25***l* and **103**.

2. The Castellani Register under this number lists a necklace; the original number may be 739 under which seven small amber fibulae are listed. This number is placed in square brackets in the catalogue.

i. L. 2·1 cm., W. 1·7 cm. Reg. 72 6-4 663 [739]

Three segments. Did not originally belong. Remains of bronze tube (?) in one end segment. Amber as above. For bronze tubes inside amber beads see *NS* 1963, figs. 53*i*, 94*l*.

25. PLATE XI

a. L. 6 cm., W. 3·7 cm. Reg. 72 6-4 723

Five segments (2 gold leaf, 3 amber). As in all examples of this type, the gold leaf is fixed on wooden segments, turned down over the ends and held by rivets on the underside. The gold and amber segments are of approximately the same width in this example; in the others the gold is often narrower. The amber is similar in all three segments; it is deep red in colour, dulled and cracked on the surface with some patches of buff patination. The ends of the segments are rounded, with the tool marks still clear on the preserved surfaces. Together the segments make an elongated oval in plan. The gold leaf is decorated by chevron hatching.

b. L. 3·7 cm., W. 2·6 cm. L. (of catch-plate) 3·1 cm. Reg. 72 6-4 725

Five segments (2 gold, 3 amber) slightly more trapezoidal in plan than *a*. Amber as *a*. Single wide boring in end segments. Part of the bronze bow, catch-plate and pin preserved.

c. L. 3·5 cm., W. 2·5 cm. Reg. 72 6-4 729

Five segments (2 gold, 3 amber). Shape as *b*, amber as *a*; end segments pitted. Single wide borings in the end segments; centre segment has three borings.

d. L. 3·4 cm., W. 2·6 cm. Reg. 72 6-4 726

Five segments (2 gold, 3 amber). Shape more trapezoidal, the centre segment being cut to a point at the sides. Remains of the spring and part of the bow still in the amber. Single boring in end segments; triple boring in the centre segment. Amber like *a*; slight pitting. The amber segments seem to belong together.

e. L. 3·3 cm., W. 2·7 cm. Reg. 72 6-4 733

Five segments (2 gold, 3 amber). Shape as *d*. Segments probably did not originally belong. Amber as *a*.

f. 3·1 cm., W. 2·7 cm. Reg. 72 6-4 727

Five segments (2 gold, 3 amber). Shape as *d*. The segments did not originally belong together. Amber as *a*.

g. L. 3·3 cm., W. 2·7 cm. Reg. 72 6-4 728

Five segments (2 gold, 3 amber). Shape and amber as *f*. The segments did not originally belong together. The end segments have single boring; middle segment triple boring.

h. L. 3·1 cm., W. 2·7 cm. Reg. 72 6-4 730

Five segments (2 gold, 3 amber). Shape and amber as *f*, but rather lighter in surface colour. The segments did not originally belong together.

i. L. 2·9 cm., W. 2·5 cm. Reg. 72 6-4 728

Five segments (2 gold, 3 amber). Shape and amber as *f*.

j. L. 2·8 cm., W. 2·4 cm. Reg. 72 6-4 731

Five segments (2 gold, 3 amber). Shape and amber as *f*.

k. L. 4·9 cm., W. 3·7 cm. Reg. 72 6-4 724

Nine segments (4 gold, 5 amber). The amber varies in colour. Made up to a trapezoidal shape but the segments did not originally belong together. The central segment is bored nine times.

l. L. 1·8 cm., W. 1·4 cm. Reg. 72 6-4 1011

Three segments (1 gold, 2 amber). Made up from different fragments, incorporating the remains of the bow of a fibula.

m. L. 1·5 cm., W. 1·4 cm. Reg. 72 6-4 732

Three segments (1 gold, 2 amber).

26. PLATE XII

a. L. 3·8. cm., W. 4 cm. Reg. 72 6-4 738

Seven segments; deep red translucent amber, dull on the surface. Although this is an excellent example of the type, it is clear that the segments did not originally belong together; they do not fit one another nor do the borings correspond.

b. L. (of fibula) 9 cm. Reg. 72 6-4 735

Five segments; arranged loosely on the bow of a bronze fibula. Amber as *a*. They did not originally belong together. Two of the segments fit together but all of them have been broken and could have been attached to the bow after the spring had been coiled. The bronze bow is rectangular in section and the long tapering catch-plate has one serrated edge.

c. L. (of fibula) 5 cm., L. (of amber) 3 cm., W. 2·7 cm. Reg. 72 6-4 736

Five segments, attached firmly to the bow of the bronze fibula, the pin of which is missing. Amber as *a*. The central segment has multiple borings; the others do not seem to belong with it.

d. L. 2·8 cm., W. 2·8 cm. Reg. 72 6-4 738

Five segments, recomposed in recent times. Amber as *a*. The segments have multiple borings which do not seem to correspond.

27. PLATE XII

a. L. (of fibula) 7·5 cm., L. (of amber) 3·6 cm., W. 4·1 cm. Reg. 72 6-4 734

Five segments make up the body of the fibula which has three long flutings. Deep red translucent amber, dull on the surface. The bronze pin, long catchplate, spring and bow are all intact and the amber is still firmly attached to the bow. It seems that there were two end segments of some perishable material that are now lost.

b. L. 2·5 cm., W. 3·2 cm. Reg. 72 6-4 737

Three segments (2 fragmentary) making up the middle portion of a trapezoidal fibula, the top of which has two longitudinal flutings. Amber as *a*. The segments do not belong together; in one of the borings through the central segment there is still the remains of a substance which was used to fill the holes in order to give a decorative effect when seen through the amber (see p. 15).

c. L. 2·6 cm., W. 2·5 cm. Reg. 72 6-4 737

Three segments forming a trapezoidal shape with five flutings on the top. Amber as *a*. These segments did not originally belong together.

d. L. 2·5 cm., W. 2·5 Reg. 72 6-4 737

Three segments (1 fragmentary) making up a trapezoidal shape with four flutings on the top. Amber as *a*. The central segment has three borings.

28. PLATE XII

L. 2·4 cm., W. 2 cm. Reg. 72 6-4 663]739]

Amber piece from the bow of a fibula. The shape is like to bows of no. **24**, but composed of a single piece of amber. The amber is bright red translucent of shattered texture and retains a high surface polish.

ITALIC

29. Segments from iron fibulae PLATE XIII

a. L. 3·5 cm., W. 3·8 cm., H. 2·5 cm. Reg. WT 1476 (Old Cat. no. 30)

Deep red translucent amber, dulled on the surface; very little patination. The amber is oval in section with its long axis at right angles to the bow of the fibula. Probably the central section of a bow of leech-type; the remaining segments, perhaps one on either side, were also of amber or some perishable material. There are three borings through the segment. In the centre one is the remains of the iron bow of the fibula. One of the side borings contains the remains of what seems to be a lining material, perhaps a pigment; the other is empty.

This piece, with *b* and *c*, was bequeathed by Sir William Temple, and is said to come from Armento in the Basilicata. The amber and iron fibulae of this type come from S. Italy, cf. von Duhn-Messerschmidt, p. 289 (from Ordona in Apulia).

b. L. 3·4 cm., W. 3·7 cm., H. 2·3 cm. Reg. WT 1477 (Old Cat. no. 31)

Amber as *a*, chipped at one end. There is a deep crack on one side. In form and dimensions similar to *a*. Three borings of which the middle one contains part of the iron bow; traces of filling in other borings. The worked ends of the segment are very well preserved and show the marks of tooling very clearly; the parallel lines of a narrow rasp criss-cross over the surface.

c. L. 4·8 cm., W. 5·1 cm., H. 3·1 cm. Reg. WT 1478 (Old Cat. no. 32)

Amber is dull and mottled on the surface; cracked across and re-joined. Similar to *a* but larger. The segment is bored ten times along its length. In the centre boring is the remains of the iron bow. In section the piece is egg-shaped rather than oval.

30. Part of a bronze fibula PLATE XIV

L. 9·7 cm. Reg. 90 5-12 6 (*BMC Bronzes*, 2011)

The fibula has a spiral disc foot engraved with geometric ornament of fine lines, swastikas and lozenges. On the bow were a series of small amber beads (and perhaps beads of other materials) one of which still survives; in a sketch in the Register of Antiquities two beads are shown.

Similar fibulae of eighth and seventh century B.C. date have been found in Etruria, Latium and the Bolognese. The type is Sundwall B III d 1. The same type of fibula sometimes has amber or bone and amber segments (Montelius Series B, pl. 177).

Bought from the Rev. G. J. Chester; said to have been found near Rome.

31. Fibula with the bow composed of amber beads and bronze discs PLATE XIV

L. (of fibula) 15·6 cm. The largest bead is 1·9 cm. in diameter — Reg. H 30 (*BMC Bronzes* 2017)

Red translucent amber, lightly patinated. Disc fibula, the spiral disc decorated with incised ornament of lines, zigzags and crosses. The bow is formed of segments, each composed of five bronze discs, separated by amber beads. Four of the beads are biconical in shape and the fifth (nearest the foot) is a smaller conical bead.

The form of the disc is common on fibulae in Benacci II contexts, *cf.* the fibula from a Pozzo grave at Tarquinia (Sundwall, p. 114, B III c 9, abb. 143) where the bow of the fibula is composed of bronze discs set close together; the combination of bronze discs and amber beads is not mentioned by Sundwall. Bow fibulae with bronze discs and amber segments are found at Tarquinia, Falerii and elsewhere (Sundwall, p. 191 = Åberg, *Chronologie* i, p. 67, abbs. 180–1); amber beads strung on the bow are also common (e.g. Montelius, pl. 282). Although there seems to be no precise parallel for this example, the total effect is very similar to one completely of bronze from Falerii (Montelius, Series B pl. 331).

Hamilton Collection; no provenience.

32. Bronze fibula with amber and glass beads PLATE XIII

L. 6·4 cm. — Reg. 90 5-12 13 (*BMC Bronzes* 2028)

The fibula has a serpentine bow with double coil and a spiral disc foot. Threaded on the pin are five beads, two of amber and three of blue glass. The general type is Sundwall D II, *β*d 1).

Bought from the Rev. G. J. Chester; said to have been found near Rome.

33. Bronze fibula with piece of amber on bow PLATE XIII

L. (of amber) 10·4 cm., H. 7·2 cm. — Reg. H 32

Orange-red opaque amber; rough surface with very slight patination and some surface cracking. The amber is broken in two pieces, large parts of the surface have flaked off, and there is a rectangular sinking at one end into which a patch was once inserted.

Only the bow and spring of the fibula survive, together with the large semicircular piece of amber of rather thin section that decorated the bow. This type of fibula is very common in Iron Age Italy (Blinkenberg *Fibules*, p. 283 and examples listed by Sundwall, pp. 193–5). The larger examples seem to come from Picenum, exclusively in female burials (e.g. the two examples from the Necropolis at Montecassiano now in the Museo Nazionale delle Marche at Ancona). Smaller examples (like no. **34**) have been found in Benacci I and II contexts in the Bolognese (*Civiltà del Ferro*, p. 616), in Etruria proper (e.g. Tarquinia, Montelius, pl. 282) and in Latium (e.g. Esquiline Necropolis, *MA* xv, 1905, pl. XIII). A related type also occurs in Hallstatt C in Central Europe (Åberg, *Chronologie*, ii, p. 32, fig. 38).

Hamilton Collection; no provenience.

34. Bronze fibula with piece of amber on the bow PLATE XIII

L. (of fibula) 6 cm.,
(of amber) 2·6 cm. × 2·6 cm. Reg. H 33

Dark red translucent amber with cracked and mottled surface.

The type is similar to no. 32, but the amber is oval in shape. The amber is now loose; originally it may have been set horizontally or vertically on the bow. There is a very similar fibula from the Esquiline cemetery (*MA* xv, 1905, pl. XIII).

Hamilton Collection; no provenience.

35. Group of a satyr and a maenad PLATE XV

H. 17·3 cm., W. 9·5 cm., thickness (max.) 4·5 cm. Reg. 65 1-3 46

Red translucent amber, dull and cracked on the surface; some slight pitting, especially at the back. The deep cavities in the amber are natural. The piece is very well preserved with only a few small pieces broken off. Below the knee of the satyr there is a row of mouldings and a terminal in the form of a dolphin which is bored through for suspension. There are several other borings which were plugged with amber, probably of a different colour. They are a common feature in carvings of this class.

The figures are carved in low relief and most skilfully adapted to the irregularities of the shape of the natural piece of amber. On the right kneels a bearded male figure with a large head and heavy body; on the left, a female figure wearing a voluminous himation is apparently in vigorous movement with her right leg off the ground and her left drawn up in an energetic jump. Between the two stands a hind on its rear legs with its head twisted round towards the male figure. The female rests her right hand on her knee and her left is behind the head of the male figure; the male, whose pose with head in profile and body in three-quarter view also suggests strong physical effort, holds his left arm above his head with the hand resting on or holding the head of the female. Another hand, presumably his right, is carved on the edge of the piece behind the drapery of the female figure. On the back is carved in low relief a coiling serpent with bearded head. It bears no obvious relation to the subject on the front.

The scene was interpreted by Kredel (*JdI* xxxviii–xxxix, 1923–4, p. 178 ff.) as a gigantomachy, with the female figure representing Artemis; the serpent, though anatomically unconnected with the male figure, was thought to support this interpretation. But the group is more simply explained as a satyr and a maenad. Although the sculptor has not succeeded in making obvious the relationship between the two, it looks more as if the male is attempting to molest the female than to engage in a death struggle with her. A serpent, moreover, also appears on no. **36**, representing a satyr vintaging.

The features of the two figures show many of the characteristic details of sub-archaic amber carving in S. Italy. The large eyes, small nose and mouth, the hair rendered by parallel engraved lines, the ears in relief but without detail. The group as a whole is the largest and most ambitious of all the 'Italic' ambers. A number of other pieces may be grouped together with it, especially two pieces in the Louvre (one of them also a rape scene), the British Museum satyr no. **36** and a fragment in the Metropolitan Museum (Richter, *Etruscan Collection*, fig. 99). The style of the heads corresponds with the group of head-pendants nos. **44** ff. (see above, p. 30).

There is some doubt as to where this piece was found. It was acquired by the Museum from the Pourtalès sale, and, according to Panofka (*Antiques du Cabinet du Conte du Pourtalès-Gorga*, Paris, 1834, pl. XX) was found at Ruvo. But Panofka adds that it was found in a tomb with the gold crown now in Munich which W. Christ (*Führer durch das K. Antiquarium in Munich*, Munich, 1903, p. 39) says was found at Armento. Panofka also seems to include in the same tomb the Sangiorgio ambers which Detken says came from Canosa.

For this piece see also C. Albizzati, *Rassegna d'arte antica e moderna*, 1919, pp. 183–200 and A. W. Franks in *Congrès International d'Anthropologie et d'Archéologie Préhistoriques*, VIII Session, Budapest, 1876, pp. 183–200.

36. Satyr vintaging PLATE XVI

H. 11·5 cm., W. (max.) 10 cm., thickness 5·7 cm. Reg. 73 8-20 695

Light red translucent amber, dull and cracked on the surface; there are patches of light patination. This piece is bored at the lower end, across the satyr's knee, presumably for suspension. There are a number of holes drilled into the amber and subsequently plugged with what seems to be a darker amber.

The figure of a satyr is carved in low relief on an unworked lump of amber. He kneels to right and is nude but for a piece of drapery knotted round his chest and draped over his right arm. His right hand holds the mouth of a wine-skin which rests on the top of his head, with its farther side carved on the back of the lump; in his raised left hand he holds a bunch of grapes. On the right of the piece is a vine with bunches of grapes and to the right of that, on the edge and partly on the back of the lump, is a bearded serpent, coiled and rearing its head. Lying on its side between the satyr and the tree is a pointed amphora with fluted body. The legs of the satyr are carved in profile on the bottom edge of the lump, the sculptor having used the edges and the deep natural cavities to give an impression of three-dimensionality. The carving is of a high quality, particularly effective in the rendering of the satyr's lean body with fine grooved lines to show the sinews. Within the limits of the lump's formlessness the anatomy is well thought out. The face is carved with great care using the normal conventions of sub-archaic amber sculpture—striated hair and beard and large semi-frontal eye.

The piece was purchased from Alessandro Castellani and comes from the collection of Prince Sangiorgio Spinelli (Detken, *Ambers*, pl. VII and VIII). All the amber in this collection is said to come from Canosa. Schultz (*BdI* 1843, p. 39), mentioned a fragment of a similar piece in the collection of Signor de Jorio who also had an amber ram and a lion from the Basilicata.

37. 'Atlas' PLATE XVII

H. 7·3 cm., W. 6·5 cm., thickness (max.) 3·3 cm. Reg. 73 8-20 697

Red translucent amber, cracked and dull on the surface. There are two deep natural cavities in the front surface, one of which goes right through the amber. The piece is bored for suspension across the head of the figure.

A male figure, nude to the waist, is carved in low relief on a roughly rectangular lump of amber of irregular thickness. His body down to the waist is shown on the front of the piece while the lower part and the feet (in profile) are carved on the back and right side of the lump. The position of the feet is such that, supposing the amber to be suspended and then turned through 180° so that the back is showing, they will be the right way up. The figure raises his arms with the elbows bent. The right hand is turned upwards and appears to be gripping something while the left has the fingers extended upwards and is shown as seen from the back. The combined action of the two hands gives the impression that they are supporting a burden; if so, the burden seems formless but it might be a wineskin. The himation draped round the lower part of the body lies in formal wedge-shaped folds across the waist with parallel grooves indicating the sweeping folds below. The head is large and heavy chinned, the eyes are pointed oval in shape, the nose and mouth small; the hair is rendered by parallel vertical grooves on the forehead. The anatomy is badly co-ordinated and ill-proportioned and the carving, on the whole, is careless.

Source as no. **36** (Detken, *Ambers*, pl. IV).

38. Four-horse chariot PLATE XVIII

H. 12 cm., W. 11·7 cm., thickness (max.) 4 cm. Reg. 73 8-20 696

Light red translucent amber with dull, cracked surface. Large parts of the surface are worn and pitted and the amber has patches of deep brown colour. There is a deep natural cavity and one artificial bore-hole in the back; the piece was suspended by means of two horizontal borings through a projecting piece at the top.

The figures are carved in low relief on a thin, roughly rectangular, piece of amber. On the main side is a chariot of four prancing horses moving to the left. Of the chariot itself only one wheel, much smaller in scale than the horses, is shown just behind the tail of the horse in the foreground. The charioteer stands holding the reins in his left hand and an unexplained object in his upturned right hand. Over his left shoulder is a belt, perhaps for a quiver; he wears a conical cap (*tutulus*). The four horses are shown with the more distant a nose in front of its nearer neighbour; the nearest horse has a long thin body, large head and sturdy legs.

The reverse subject seems to be unrelated. The head of the farthest horse in the *quadriga* corresponds with a horse-like head on the reverse, belonging apparently to a hippocamp, though the rest of its anatomy is hard to follow. Holding the head of this creature by means of a long rope is a nude youth, sitting on its back. The rear part of the hippocamp is shown behind him. The youth has a cap on his head and a belt around his waist; his features are a little clearer than those of the charioteer on the obverse.

The style of this group seems closely connected with Etruscan work and this may be explained, as suggested in the introduction, p. 31, if we suppose it was made in Campania or under the influence of Etrusco-Campanian art.

Source as no. **36** (Detken, *Ambers*, pls. V–VI).

39. Female figure PLATE XVII

H. 6·5 cm., W. 6·6 cm., thickness (max.) 2·1 cm. Reg. 73 8-20 698

Light red translucent amber, dulled on the surface; slight pitting at the back. The back of the lump is unworked but has been smoothed. The boring for suspension runs across near the top of the piece; the lower part of the figure is broken off.

A female figure is carved in low relief on a formless lump of amber; her head is in profile, her body in three-quarter view. She wears a chiton of heavy stuff falling in parallel folds and perhaps a second garment on her left arm. Her head is inclined towards the pomegranate and palm-leaf(?) which she holds in her left hand; her right arm, held downwards and bent at the elbow, holds rings or a wreath. Above on her right shoulder stands an owl. She wears her hair in a *sphendone* with a fringe, shown by parallel vertical grooves, on the forehead. The features, particularly the large frontal eye and the nose, remind one strongly of nos. **35–36.** The various attributes suggest that the figure is a goddess and the owl and the drapery indicate Athena. If so, the iconography is rather unconvincing.

Source as no. **36** (Detken, *Ambers*, pl. IV).

40. Male figure seated PLATE XVII

H. 11 cm., W. (max.) 5·8 cm., thickness 1·5 cm. Reg. 77 8-12 1

Red translucent amber, dulled and pitted on the surface. The figure is pierced through the head for suspension. There are a number of cavities bored in the amber, one on the right forearm and another just below the arm; there are also three borings in the back. The amber has been cut into just behind the right forearm and through the buttocks; the right foot of the figure is broken off by reason of a similar cut made across the amber.

The figure of a youth is carved 'à jour' on a thin piece of amber left irregular at the back and carefully smoothed on the front. He appears to be sitting, but the pose is not easy to interpret. While his legs are bent in a sitting position there is no clear indication of a seat and the position of the left foot with the toe pointing upwards is difficult to explain. The youth clasps his right hand round the end of a thin stick; his other arm and hand do not appear. He wears a piece of drapery arranged in tight parallel folds around his waist and between his legs (*cf.* the garment worn by the Satyr vintaging, no. **36**). His head is inclined forward and the hair is fringed on the forehead and falls in a long bun down the back of the neck; the top of the head is left smooth as though there were a head cloth or cap over it. The style and detail of drapery strongly recall nos. **35–36.**

The piece was purchased from M. Sambon; there is no information as to where it was found.

41. Pendant in the form of a nude kouros PLATE XIX

H. 5·8 cm., W. (max.) 2·5 cm., thickness 1·2 cm. Reg. WT 1456 (Old Cat. no. 15)

Red translucent amber with patchy patina over the whole surface. Both legs of the figure are broken off above the knee. The top of the head has a bead-and-reel moulding which is pierced for suspension; the hole is now blocked.

The figure stands with arms held tightly to the sides and fists clenched. The left leg is slightly advanced. The anatomy is well modelled in front and rather flatly at the back. The broad shoulders and narrow waist recall early Greek kouroi but the details of the face, with its pointed oval eyes, triangular nose and small mouth put the figure in the same group as the head pendants nos. **54–60.** The hair lies in waves on the forehead and in long striations at the back of the head coming down on to the shoulders.

Comparable pendant figures are two *korai* in Dresden (Pelka, *Bernstein*, p. 28, fig. 12), the group of a woman and child in the Metropolitan Museum, New York (Richter, *Etruscan Collection*, p. 32, figs. 104–5). A closely related figure in ivory was found in Etruria together with nine pieces of amber (including three hares and a ram's head) (K. A. Neugebauer, *Antiken in deutschem Privatbesitz*, Berlin, 1938, nos. 255–6).

Bequeathed by Sir William Temple; said to come from Armento.

42. Pendant in the form of a human figure PLATE XIX

H. 6·2 cm., W. 2 cm., thickness (max.) 1·5 cm. Reg. 73 8-20 713

Red translucent amber, dull and cracked on the surface. The figure has been broken across the shoulders and restored with the missing parts, including most of the left arm, supplied in wax. The piece is bored for suspension across the head and there is another boring into the amber just by the left arm.

The figure, probably female, stands frontal with the arms held rigidly to the sides. The only garment is a cloak which is indicated by a series of diagonal grooves passing over the left shoulder. The carving is altogether very summary. The eyes are bulging and shapeless, the nose is a rough triangle and the mouth is hardly shown at all. The hands are not carved; the arms merely taper to a point. The back is unworked. The hair on the forehead is not engraved but a headband is indicated round the back of the head.

The figure was acquired from Alessandro Castellani and according to the Register, was in the collection of Prince Sangiorgio Spinelli; but it is not illustrated in Detken's catalogue. It is a piece much inferior to the majority of the S. Italian carvings and may be compared with a little figure pendant in the National Museum at Belgrade from Novi Pazar, which is one of a group of amber carvings perhaps imported from Italy including some of the characteristic ram's head pendants. It may also be compared with some of the poorer pieces found in the Bolognese.

43. Group of two standing figures PLATE XIX

H. 7 cm., W. (max.) 3·9 cm., thickness (max.) 1·4 cm. Reg. 59 12-26 833

Dark red translucent amber, dull on the surface. The figures have been badly damaged about the legs and restored in plaster; there are small plaster restorations on the heads and faces. The group was not meant to stand up and is pierced for suspension just below the ear of the man in front.

The two figures stand one behind the other on a single base. The figure in front is a bearded fat man standing with his left leg advanced. His right arm is bent at the elbow with the hand resting on his stomach, and his left arm is held with the hand up to the side of his face. His hair is long and parted in the centre; his face slopes backward from a strong chin, his nose is short and pointed and his eyes are long and oval with sharply marked eyebrow ridges. Behind this man, and standing close up against him, is a second figure whose sex is less certain but is probably female. This figure is beardless and wears a tunic reaching to the thighs; the hair is long and parted in the centre and is tied with a band behind the neck. Only one leg is shown and this is marked with vertical grooves presumably intended to show drapery. The right hand is held against the side and holds an L-shaped object; the left hand is held up to the breast and seems to be clenched.

In the Register of Antiquities the amber is included as the last item in a collection 'excavated by C. T. Newton', but without specific provenience. The evidence of style points to it being Etruscan work a good deal earlier in date than the series of 'Italic' amber carvings. Nothing closely comparable has been found but the detail of the heads and hairdressing may be compared with a pendant in the form of the upper part of two male figures found at Castelbellino (*MA* xxxv, 1935, p. 419, fig. 46) in Picenum. A series of two-figure groups in rough 'Etruscanising' style of the seventh or early sixth centuries B.C. from Satricum in Latium include figures back to back and frontally side by side. They are not closely related to our group but might well be local imitations of Etruscan work not unlike ours. Other Etruscan amber figure carvings of the sixth century B.C. include a *kouros* from Arezzo (*SE* i, 1927 Tav. VIII) and a little figurine of Venus Pudica (Dohan, *Tomb Groups*, Narce Tomb 23M).

44. Frontal female head

PLATE XX

H. 4·9 cm., W. 4 cm., thickness 2 cm. Reg. 73 8-20 703

Deep red translucent amber, the surface reddy-brown. The cracking of the amber gives a semi-opaque look to exposed surfaces. There are several borings into the amber. One, formed by two borings sloping downwards from either end runs across the top and there is a second from front to back with a vertical boring into it. There are two borings into the lower surface.

The hair is shown as superimposed wavy ridges on the forehead and above the hair is the beginning of a head-cloth marked by a groove and ridge with a flat surface above. The features are accurately carved; the large triangular eyes, the small nose and the mouth are very similar to the features of the profile head no. **52**. The eyebrows are sharp ridges and the nose and mouth are also very angular in form. The head is cut flat across the top and bottom. The ears are concealed by circular earrings.

The head was purchased from Alessandro Castellani and is said to come from the collection of Prince Sangiorgio Spinelli (see under no. **36**); it is not illustrated in Detken's Catalogue. Together with nos. **45–53** it forms a group closely related in style and characterised by flat archaic features with large almond eyes, small nose and mouth, hatched or parallel waved hair. The distribution and probable centres of manufacture for this type of head-pendant are discussed in the introduction, p. 29ff.

The heads were made as components of necklaces or fibulae and are either bored for suspension on the top of the head or down their length for stringing on the bow of a fibula. An example in Munich has a bronze ring and loop fixed on the top of the head (Inv. no. 15.003).

45. Frontal female head — PLATE XX

H. 5·3 cm., W. 3·4 cm., thickness 2·1 cm. — Reg. 73 8-20 704

Red translucent amber, dulled on the surface; some slight pitting. The top of the head is badly broken and the suspension boring across the top shows in section. There is a round depression, presumably a flaw in the amber, on the right cheek and a deep cavity behind it. On the back there are three apparently artificial borings into the amber.

Frontal head carved from a shapeless lump of amber worked to rounded form at the front. The hair lies in superimposed waves on the forehead and is surrounded by a double ridge with a flat surface above it, suggesting a head-cloth.

Source as no **44**. (Detken, *Ambers*, pl. II, top left). There is a larger head in a very similar style from Roccanova in Lucania (Biagliati, *Museo di Taranto*, p. 27 & 68, *Ori e Argenti*, no. 319).

46. Frontal female head — PLATE XX

H. 6 cm., W. 5·5 cm., thickness (max.) 3 cm. — Reg. WT 1446 (Old Cat. no. 5)

Deep red, semi-opaque amber with some surface pitting and retaining some shine. The amber is pierced horizontally at the top for suspension; there are other borings, some of them plugged with amber(?).

The head is carved in a rough lump of amber rounded on one side into a regular shape. The carving is very assured. The forehead hair is shown by engraved lines on either side of a central parting; the ears are in relief but without detail. The eyes are in the shape of triangles rounded at the apex; an engraved line marks the eyebrow. Nose and mouth are carefully modelled. The hair above the forehead is bound in a head-cloth and behind the left ear there is hatching of a rough kind which may be intended, as on other examples, to represent hair.

The head was bequeathed by Sir William Temple, and, like all the Temple ambers, is said to come from Armento. It is very similar in detail to no. **47**, which is a Castellani piece from Canosa.

47. Frontal female head PLATE XX

H. 5·9 cm., W. 5 cm., thickness 3 cm. Reg. 73 8-20 700

Light red translucent amber, dull on the surface. The modelling much worn down. The amber is pierced vertically with a wide boring, 1 cm. in diam. There are also two borings into the head just below the top which have been plugged with amber(?) and two unfinished borings in the top surface.

Carved from a rough lump left in its natural shape at the back and worked to a regular form at the front. The forehead hair is rendered with a central parting and hatched in different directions on either side; above the forehead, the hair seems to be contained in a head-cloth. Eyes, nose and full-lipped mouth are very similar to no. **46**. The ears are carefully and simply modelled. There is hatching below the ear on the left-side, mainly on the back of the piece (*cf.* no. **49–50**).

Source as no. **44** (Detken, *Ambers*, pl. III, top right).

48. Frontal female head PLATE XXI

H. 6 cm., W. 5·5 cm., thickness (max.) 3 cm. Reg. 73 8-20 701

Red translucent amber; surface dull with patches of deep oxidation patina. At the bottom may be seen the remains of an iron rod passing through the amber and suggesting that the head decorated the bow of a fibula.

The head is carved from a rough lump of amber, unworked at the back. The style is rough but the face symmetrical and accurately carved. The forehead hair is shown by vertical hatching; the hair on the crown is contained in a head-cloth. The eyes are large and pointed oval in shape. Nose and mouth are small. The ears are roughly carved and badly misplaced.

Source as no. **44** (Detken, *Ambers*, pl. III, bottom right).

49. Frontal female head PLATE XXI

H. 7·8 cm., W. 7 cm., thickness (max.) 3·5 cm. Reg. 73 8-20 699

Red translucent amber clouded and cracked on the surface. Bored for suspension across the top of the head, almost to its full width, with borings from either end meeting in the centre of the top. There are numerous other borings into the amber most of which have been subsequently filled up with a darker coloured amber.

The head is carved from a rough lump of amber, the irregularities of which distort the features. The hair is shown by diagonal hatching on the forehead; above the forehead the smooth surface and the ridge suggest a cap or head-cloth. The ears are in relief. The eyes are large, triangular in shape with rounded apex, and slant upwards. The nose is long and narrow, the mouth thin and mean. One curious feature is the lines engraved on the right cheek which, if the conventions are consistent, ought to be hair; there are no corresponding lines on the other cheek.

Source as no. **44** (Detken, *Ambers*, pl. III, top left).

50. Frontal female head PLATE XXI

H. 6·5 cm., W. 4·6 cm., thickness (max.) 2·3 cm. Reg. 73 8-20 702

Red translucent amber with surface cracking and clouding. Badly worn, bored horizontally across the top for suspension. Several other borings in the amber, some of which were plugged.

The head is carved from a rough piece of amber, probably shaped on one side before carving the face. The head is in very rough style. The hair is shown by vertical hatching on the forehead and is contained in a head-cloth or cap. The eyes are large and pointed oval in shape. Nose, mouth and chin form a pyramidical sequence widening downwards. There is some attempt to show the ears. On the left cheek the engraved lines are similar to those of no. **49** and must represent hair.

Source as no. **44** (Detken, *Ambers*, pl. III, bottom left).

51. Female head PLATE XXII

H. 4·2 cm., W. 2·4 cm., thickness (max.) 3·4 cm. Reg. 73 8-20 706

Dark red translucent amber, dulled, with brownish tints on the surface. The nose seems to have been re-fixed. The boring for suspension runs from the top of the head to the back of the right side. There are three disfiguring holes in the amber on the left .

A rough lump of amber carved in the form of a female head. The amber has been worked up to give the face symmetry and good proportions but the head is deformed to the shape of the amber. The hair is shown by fine hatching on the forehead and on the crown is contained by a head-band. A large bulge on the right side below the ear and a smaller bulge on the left are both engraved to represent hair. In shape the head, with the large eyes, small nose and mouth, is very similar to nos. **44–50**. The chin is well modelled and some of the upper part of the neck is shown. The face is long and thin. The features are less barbaric than those of the frontal heads.

Source as no. **44** (Detken, *Ambers*, pl. IIA).

52. Female head in profile PLATE XXII

L. 7·3 cm., W. (max.) 3·3 cm. Reg. 73 8-20 705

Red translucent amber, dulled on the surface and slightly pitted; the chin is damaged. The piece is bored for suspension near the top of the head and there are remains of bronze wire(?) still in the hole. It has been cut into two facets at the back. The cutting, which is unusual, may be explained by the fact that the amber was put to some other use before being carved as a head-pendant.

Female head in profile to the left, carved from a narrow tapering lump of amber. The hair lies in deep waves on the forehead and is contained in a cap or head-cloth. The eye is very large and shown almost in frontal view; nose and mouth are small and delicately carved. A small part of the neck is shown with a series of engraved lines at the back (*cf.* no. **46**). This head, like the frontal heads, is a component of a necklace. A necklace found in the excavation of the Certosa site at Bologna (Tomb 100) incorporates pendants of this type (rougher in style) with rams' heads, formless lumps and beads. At Marzabotto (G. Gozzadini, *Ulteriori scoperte* pl. 15), rams' heads, a hippocamp(?), profile and frontal heads were combined. No doubt, pieces of this quality were also combined with cowrie shell pendants (no. **94**) and ram's head pendants (nos. **81–88**). Similar profile pendants have been found at Populonia (*NS* 1926, p. 326) and at Spina (Tombs, Valle Pega 640B and 514A). There is also a similar piece in the museum at Bari (inv. no. 6598).

Source as no. **44** (Detken, *Ambers*, pl. II, top right).

53. Female head in profile PLATE XXII

H. 4·5 cm., W. 4·1 cm., thickness (max.) 2 cm. Reg. 73 8-20 707

Red translucent amber, dull and cracked on the surface; very slight oxidation patina at the back. Suspension was by a boring across the corner of the lump behind the head, so that the piece hung with head looking downwards. There are a number of natural cavities at the back of the amber but no artificial ones.

The head is carved on a rough lump of amber, unworked at the back. The eye is large and shown frontal; nose, chin and mouth are in pyramidal sequence. The hair is bound with a head-cloth, the bands of which are shown by shallow grooves; these bands are continued on the amber behind the head. This piece is second-rate work, comparable in style and quality with no. **50**.

Source as no. **44** (Detken, *Ambers*, pl. II, bottom right).

54. Frontal female head PLATE XXIII

H. 7 cm., W. 4·5 cm., thickness 3·2 cm. Reg. WT 1444 (Old Cat. no. 3)

Red translucent amber very badly pitted on top of the head and at the back. Very dark surface colour. On top of the head is a bead-and-reel hollowed out for suspension.

This head is the finest of the series of pendants (nos. **54–60**) carved in a fully rounded style with the detail of the face well-proportioned and delicately modelled. The hair is shown in waves on the forehead, the eyes are small and narrow, the thin mouth turns up in a gentle smile. The chin is strong and the ears are carefully modelled.

This series of heads include five examples (of which this is one) bequeathed by Sir William Temple and said to come from Armento. This piece is probably the earliest in date, still in the sixth century B.C.; no. **60** (a male head?) is the latest and probably dates from around 450 B.C. The heads seem to form a group with some other surviving figured ambers which is discussed in the introduction on p. 30). There are several similar heads, one in Lyon and another in Dresden, which have the same bead-and-reel for suspension on top of the head. A head in New York (Richter, *Etruscan Collection*, fig. 101, p. 32), two heads in Stuttgart, and one in Munich (Inv. no. 15004) are comparable in style. The provenience of this type, where it is known, is always South Italy, and it is interesting that there are no examples of this type among the heads said to come from Canosa.

55. Frontal female head PLATE XXIII

H. 4·6 cm., W. 5·2 cm., thickness (max.) 2·2 cm. Reg. 65 12-14 75

Red translucent amber very badly cracked and pitted on the surface. Suspension by a boring across the top of the head. The back is left rough, and there is a large dent in the amber above the forehead.

The deterioration of the surface is such that the features are barely recognizable but it is clear that the head must have been similar to no. **54**. The eyes, mouth and nose are very like in detail. The ears are carved, the hair probably waved on the forehead.

This piece was presented to the Museum under the will of Henry Christy. It presumably comes from Italy like the two ram's head pendants in the same collection.

56. Frontal female head wearing a stephane PLATE XXIII

H. 6·7 cm., W. 5·2 cm., thickness (max.) 3·2 Reg. WT 1445 (Old Cat. No. 4)

Deep red translucent amber. The patina has destroyed entirely the modelling on the left side of the face; on the right side, though the surface is dark and dulled, the profile is fairly well preserved. Suspension by two diagonal borings meeting in the centre.

The head is carved in the rounded style and is unworked at the back. The features are very similar to no. **54**, but the cheeks are fuller and the forehead less prominent. The hair lies in waves on the forehead and above it is a plain *stephane* with a narrow ridge just above the hair. The ears were not carved.

Bequeathed by Sir William Temple; said to come from Armento.

57. Frontal female head wearing a stephane PLATE XXIII

H. 5·6 cm., W. 5·5 cm., thickness (max.) 4·4 cm. Reg. WT 1443 (Old Cat. no. 2)

Dark red translucent amber, the surface marred by deep cracking and browny-yellow patina. The piece is bored across the top of the head for suspension.

Frontal head worked in full rounded style, the back also worked into a curved surface. The hair lies in waves on the forehead and is crowned by a *stephane* like the slats of a Venetian blind. The details of the face are delicately modelled. The long oval eyes and the upturned mouth combine to produce an archaic look which is not consistent with the modelling and soft transitions of the eyebrows and nose. The ears are carefully worked and large in proportion to the other features.

Bequeathed by Sir William Temple; said to come from Armento.

58. Frontal female head wearing a stephane PLATE XXIV

H. 5·3 cm., W. 3·5 cm., thickness (max.) 3 cm. Reg. WT 1447 (Old Cat. no. 7)

Deep red translucent amber, dark and deeply pitted over the surface. A through boring for suspension across the top of the head just above the *stephane*.

The features are hardly recognizable. The head is similar to nos. **54–7**. The hair lies in waves on the forehead and is topped by a *stephane*. The top of the head is rounded, the back is flat with the *stephane* continuing right round. The ears are carved in relief. The face is very square in outline; part of the neck is also carved.

Bequeathed by Sir William Temple; said to come from Armento.

59. Frontal female head wearing a stephane PLATE XXIV

H. 3·4 cm., W. 2·9 cm., thickness (max.) 2 cm. Reg. 72 6-4 1009

Red translucent amber, dark and dull on the surface; very little patination. Suspension by two borings starting just in front of the ears and meeting at the top of the head.

The head is very similar to no. **56**, with small eyes, nose and mouth. Hair lies in waves on the forehead and there is a *stephane* above. The ears are carved in relief. The top of the head is smooth and rather flat; the back is also smooth.

This head was purchased from Alessandro Castellani; it is not one of the ambers from the Sangiorgio Spinelli collection, and there is no information as to its provenience.

60. Frontal female (?) head PLATE XXIV

H. 4·9 cm., W. 3·4 cm., thickness (max.) 2·9 cm. Reg. WT 1457 (Old Cat. no. 16)

Deep red translucent amber, dull on the surface. Some pitting at the back caused by oxidation. There is a horizontal boring across the top of the head which also shows the remains of a silver (?) wire, and a larger vertical boring in the middle of the top of the head which also contains metallic remains.

The hair on the forehead divides more like male hair but is bound by a fillet. By analogy with other heads, it is probably female. The top of the head is smooth, perhaps meant to be a cap. The eyes are small below carefully modelled eyebrows, the nose is long and the mouth proportionately small. The head seems to be the latest in the series of frontal heads, perhaps of the middle of the fifth century.

Bequeathed by Sir William Temple; said to come from Armento.

61. Bearded head PLATE XXIV

H. 5·2 cm., W. 2·9 cm., thickness (max.) 1·5 cm. Reg. WT 1458 (Old Cat. no. 17)

Red translucent amber. The surface is deeply patinated to a brownish colour. Bore holes for suspension across the top of the head.

The head is carved to conform to the shape of the amber so that the features are grotesquely distorted. The side on which the face is carved is convex. The back is flattish. The face is satyr-like with large pointed oval eyes surrounded by a double line, a small flattened nose and tiny mouth. The large walrus moustache widens at the ends and is marked by grooving; on the chin lines are engraved to indicate a beard. The hair on the forehead is represented by diagonal hatching and the top of the head is plain, as though contained in a cap.

Several similar satyr-heads survive. One from Palestrina (Giglioli, pl. CCCLXXVII) is a work of better quality and two in the Museum of Fine Arts, Boston are also better work. Nearest in style and quality to this is an unpublished head in Dresden. Another satyr-head which was on the London antique market in 1952 was said to be part of a find at Metapontum.

Bequeathed by Sir William Temple, said to come from Armento.

62. Grotesque head PLATE XXIV

L. (max.) 5 cm., H. 2·8 cm., thickness (max.) 1·7 cm. Reg. 73 8-20 708

Red translucent amber cracked and dulled on the surface. The lower part of the face is broken away, the break is old, the present state of the surface being very similar to that of the worked surfaces. The amber is bored for suspension across the top of the head.

The head is carved from a shapeless lump of amber. On one side the features are semi-human with forehead hair marked by long vertical striations, a large eye, triangular in shape, and a large ass's ear. Behind the ear is a thin appendage of the amber which is grooved to represent hair. On the opposite side the carving seems to represent a horse's mane.

Bought from Alessandro Castellani; once in the collection of Prince Sangiorgio Spinelli (Detken, *Ambers*, pl. II, bottom left).

63. Relief of a lion couchant PLATE XXV

H. 4·7 cm., L. 11 cm., thickness (max.) 2·7 cm. Reg. 73 8-1 1

Deep red translucent amber with opaque brown and dark brown patination. Chipped all over; the larger chips on nose and mouth made good in wax. The back of the relief is smoothed and rounded. There is a boring for suspension through the top of the head.

The lion is in a lying position but the body is raised; the pose is a cross between lying and crouching similar to that of the lions of the Corfu pediment. The sinews of the legs are shown by grooves, the hair of the mane by cross-hatching. The tail is curled on top of the back. The head is turned three-quarters front to show both eyes; the eyes are inset with beads of blue glass paste.

The piece was purchased from a M. Boöcke and there is no information about its provenience. It is not in any way a typical 'Italic' piece and I known of nothing really comparable.

64. Pendant in the form of a lion couchant PLATE XXV

L. 6·5 cm., W. 2·7 cm., thickness 2·5 cm. Reg. WT 1449 (Old Cat. no. 8)

Red translucent amber with dull surface; large patches of pitting. The suspension was by a boring through a bead-and-reel at the tail.

The animal is in a lying position with the rear legs drawn up and the fore-paws extended. The head is turned slightly to the right and rests upon the right paw. The legs are flattened out on the under side so as to appear in full view; only the thighs and toes show in profile. The details—tail, mane, etc.—are carved in a naturalistic but summary style with very little distortion of the proportions. The tail lies on the animal's back.

This piece was bequeathed by Sir William Temple and, like the rest of the Temple ambers is said to come from Armento. The style is very close to that of some amber carvings from Belmonte Piceno (Marconi and Serra, *Il Museo Nazion-*

ale delle Marche in Ancona, p. 69). Two of these are groups depicting a lion attacking another animal, and the third is a long oval piece of amber carved at both ends into the form of a lion's head; all three served to decorate the bows of metal fibulae, the remains of which are still visible at either end. W. L. Brown (*The Etruscan Lion*, Oxford, 1960, p. 100) was inclined to think that the Belmonte ambers, because they served a purpose to which amber is commonly put in Picenum, were locally made but by an immigrant craftsman from Etruria (perhaps from Orvieto or Chiusi). There seems, however, to be very little reason for connecting this group with Etruria and the Belmonte pieces are more likely to be imports from Southern Italy (*cf.* the Falconara group in the Metropolitan Museum, New York). For the Belmonte groups see also *Guida Ancona*, p. 65, figs. pp. 48 and 70, and *MA* xxxv, 1936, pl. 30, 1–2.

65. Pendant in the form of a lion couchant PLATE XXVI

L. 4·2 cm., W. 2·2 cm., thickness ·9 cm. Reg. WT 1454 (Old Cat. no. 13)

Light red translucent amber with patches of deep patina over the whole surface. The amber was bored transversely for suspension at the tail and has broken away at this point.

The lion is lying in a position very similar to that of no. **64** with the rear leg bent up and the forelegs extended; the whole figure is flattened, and the details are carved in low relief. The tail lies over the back. The forepaws are broken off.

There is an identical piece from Belmonte Piceno in the Museum at Ancona which was used not as a pendant but as decoration for the bow of a fibula. The pendant adds some confirmation to the attribution of these pieces to S. Italy rather than Picenum because it is very close in style and form to such works as the Achelous (no. **68**).

Bequeathed by Sir William Temple; said to come from Armento.

66. Boar couchant PLATE XXVI

L. 6·7 cm., H. 2·4 cm., thickness 1·3 cm. Reg. WT 1462 (Old Cat. no. 21)

Red translucent amber, badly pitted over most of the surface. The piece is bored for suspension through the lower part of the head.

The animal is carved on both sides of a thin lump of amber. The rear legs are drawn up, the forelegs extended. The bristles on the back are rendered by a series of ridges. The ears and one eye are fairly well preserved; all the other details are damaged by pitting.

Bequeathed by Sir William Temple; said to come from Armento.

67. Ape(?) PLATE XXVI

H. 4·2 cm., L. 6·5 cm., thickness (max.) 3·3 cm. Reg. 73 8-20 710

Red translucent amber, dull and pitted on the surface. There are two borings for suspension, one beneath the right upper arm and the other across the chest. There are several broken surfaces showing a very clear red amber below the patination.

This strange figure is carved in the round and represents a four-legged animal with a human or semi-human head. The pose is a crouching one with the rear legs bent up and the forelegs, which are thinner than the rear legs, placed under the knee. Apart from the long thin 'fingers' of the forepaws no other anatomical detail is rendered. The head is turned to the right and the hair falls in a mane; the features are pointed, the mouth half-open. The whole expression is not unlike an ape or a grotesque with simian and human features.

The piece was purchased from Alessandro Castellani and said to come from the collection of Prince Sangiorgio Spinelli, but it is not in Detken's Catalogue. It has something in common with the harpy figures found at Sala Consilina and now in the Petit Palais, Paris.

68. Man-headed bull couchant (Achelous) PLATE XXVII

H. 6·3 cm., L. 12·3 cm., thickness 2·6 cm. Reg. WT 1442 (Old Cat. no. 1)

Red translucent amber with some pitting over most of the surface. Part of the genitals(?) is made of a separate piece of amber different in colour which was inset in the lower edge of the piece. The figure was a pendant, pierced for suspension at the tail end through a half-round moulding decorated with a bead-and-reel. The two diagonal borings meet in the centre of the bead-and-reel.

The figure is carved in relief and shown in profile with the rear legs bent and the head turned back. On the back the forelegs are carved in plan; the rear legs are shown in profile but with the shank and hoof on the lower edge of the amber—a good example of the liberty taken with anatomical detail to adapt a figure to the shape of the amber. The head is horned and bearded with a drooping moustache, and the details of the face are similar to the group of head-pendants (nos. **54–60**). The mane is rendered by horizontal ridges. The tail curls over the thigh.

There is a very similar but smaller carving without provenience in the Louvre (de Ridder, no. 2133). The character of the carving puts the figure into a large class which includes several other pieces in this catalogue and the similarities are so striking that one is inclined to attribute some of them (e.g. nos. **69** and **70**) to the same hand.

Bequeathed by Sir William Temple; said to come from Armento.

69. Sphinx couchant PLATE XXVIII

H. 3·7 cm., L. 6·3 cm., thickness (max.) 1·5 cm. Reg. WT 1453 (Old Cat. no. 12)

Reddy brown amber with a very dark brown surface discoloration and a shiny patina. The surface is much worn. Pierced for suspension from top to bottom through the face. On the back are three depressions which may be artificial.

The sphinx is carved on the convex side of a thin, rough piece of amber. The back is unworked. The position of the forelegs is obscured by wear. The head is turned back in profile and the features seem to have been carefully worked. The primary feathers of the wing are marked by horizontal grooves. The creature's hind-quarters are bunched up and small in proportion. The left rear leg is bent at the joints and shown in profile; the right leg is also shown so that the hind-quarters appear almost in plan—a cruel distortion. The tail seems to be indicated by a ridge following the sweep of the wing. This piece could well be by the same hand as the Achelous no. **68**.

Bequeathed by Sir WilliamTemple; said to come from Armento.

70. Gazelle(?) couchant PLATE XXVIII

L. 4·5 cm., W. 1·8 cm., thickness 1·3 cm. Reg. WT 1455 (Old Cat. no. 14)

Deep red translucent amber, dulled and cracked on the surface. The suspension was by a boring though a single astragal at the tail end of the figure.

The limbs of the animal, as in a number of other amber figures, are twisted and distorted to provide an interesting view on all sides. The amber is irregular in shape, flattish on two sides. The animal is in a lying position with fore and rear legs bent up and with his head turned back on the right side of the body. The hind legs are shown in profile but the left hind leg is twisted under the body so that the back also provides a semi-profile view of the animal. All the features are in low relief.

Style and carving remind one of the sphinx no. **69**; there is a very similar pendant among the ambers from Sala Consilina in the Petit Palais, Paris.

Bequeathed by Sir William Temple; said to come from Armento.

71. Hedgehog(?) PLATE XXVIII

H. 3·3 cm., L. 9·2 cm., thickness 1·5 cm. Reg. 73 8-20 712

Red translucent amber, dull and cracked on the surface. Nose and tail chipped. Suspension by two diagonal borings from top to bottom meeting at the tail.

This curious creature carved from a thin, flat piece of amber worked on both sides is difficult to interpret. It may be a very simplified version of a hedgehog.

The face (the end of the snout is missing) seems to be recessed into a protective coat which may be a version of the spiky coat of the hedgehog but, if so, there is no suggestion of spikes. The ridge on top of the back and the corresponding ridge underneath are unexplained. The animal seems to be lying down but the feet are not shown.

Purchased from Alessandro Castellani; from the collection of Prince Sangiorgio Spinelli (Detken, *Ambers.* pl. I F).

72. Frog or toad PLATE XXVIII

L. 6·9 cm., W. 3·7 cm. thickness 2·3 cm., Reg. WT 1448 (Old Cat. no. 7)

Red translucent amber dulled on the surface and mottled with light brown dots on the underside. Some surface pitting. The pendant is bored for suspension at the narrow end by two borings, one from each side, meeting below the mouth. There are two depressions in the amber, one between the hind legs, the other on the underside, which seem to be artificial.

Pendant, egg-shaped and flat on one side carved into the form of a stylised frog. A good simplified impression of the big crouching hind legs is given and of the tiny front legs. The face is very pointed with a fine groove to indicate the wide mouth. The shape is basically the same as that of the 'cowrie shell' pendants, no. **94**; this form and the stylisation of the creature suggest a fertility amulet.

The frog is a not uncommon subject in amber carvings. An archaic Etruscan example from Vetulonia is illustrated in *NS* 1895, pp. 311–16, fig. 33, Montelius, Series B, pl. 180. There was another frog in the Stroganoff Collection (Muñoz, pl. 47, 3). A piece much nearer the style of this one was part of a find at Metapontum (see under no. **61**). For the frog and toad as fertility symbols see O. Keller, *Die antike Tierwelt*, ii, 1913, p. 305 ff.

Bequeathed by Sir William Temple; said to come from Armento.

73. Snake(?) PLATE XXIX

H. 4·2 cm., L. 6·4 cm., thickness 2·5 cm. Reg. WT 1450 (Old Cat. no. 9)

Opaque reddy-brown amber; underneath the polished skin a deep patina. The back of the piece is smooth but unworked except for three shallow grooves at either end. At the suspension end there is a roughly carved bead-and-reel, but the suspension was through a transverse boring below it. The end of the head is broken off and most of the long pointed ear is rubbed away.

The amber is roughly oval in shape, convex on one side. On the convex side is the head of an animal carved in high relief and the long thin body or neck is marked with mane-like striations. The head is similar to no. **80** but not obviously horned. On the surface of the amber above the head and neck there is what appears to be the coil of a snake's body, marked by shallow grooves and hatching on the top edge which are presumably meant to indicate the scaly skin. The interpretation of the relief is very problematic.

Bequeathed by Sir William Temple; said to come from Armento.

74. Queer bird PLATE XXIX

H. 6·4 cm., L. 7 cm., thickness (max.) 3 cm. Reg. 73 8-20 709

Red translucent amber, dull on the surface but with very slight patination. There is one through boring and two diagonal borings for suspension on the top of the wings.

The figure is a bird with human or semi-human features. The legs and feet (which are damaged) are human rather than animal; the head is bird-like with hooked beak, large eyes and smooth domed skull. The feathers of the wings are marked by parallel ridges and grooves. The figure is perhaps thought of as semi-human and semi-bird. It is not truly carved in the round, the two sides bearing little relation to one another.

There is a figure not unlike this one, but carved in a flatter style, in the Museo Nazionale at Ancona. This piece seems to be the one mentioned in *BdI*, 1842, p. 40, where it is compared with a piece found at Armento which is described as 'una sirena disgraziatamente frantumata, con un grossa testa umana di faccia e le ali strette al dosso'.

Purchased from Alessandro Castellani; from the collection of Prince Sangiorgio Spinelli (Detken, *Ambers*, pl. I E).

75. Pendant in the form of the foreparts of a lion PLATE XXIX

L. 3·3 cm., W. 2·2 cm., thickness 1·4 cm. Reg. WT 1460 (Old Cat. no. 19)

Deep red translucent amber dulled and pitted on the surface. There is a series of grooves and ridges round the top of the pendant and on the top surface a line of interrupted bead-and-reel in relief. Bored for suspension across the top just below the bead-and-reel.

The head and forepaws of a lion are represented. All the features are carved in very low relief and the whole head is flattened to accommodate it to the shape of the amber. Nose, eyes and mouth are clustered together at the end; ears and mane are in low relief.

The detail of the lion's head is very close to the lion pendant no. **64**.

Bequeathed by Sir William Temple; said to come from Armento.

76. Pendant in the form of the foreparts of a pig PLATE XXIX

L. 3·1 cm., W. 2·4 cm., thickness 1·2 cm. Reg. WT 1459 (Old Cat. no. 18)

Light red translucent amber, dull with cracking on the surface. The features of the pig are flattened and all the details are in low relief. The forelegs are shown in relief on the underside. The upper part of the pendant and the suspension are the same as no. **75**.

The pendant belongs to the same series as the lion's head pendant no. **75**.

Bequeathed by Sir William Temple; said to come from Armento.

77. Foreparts of a boar PLATE XXIX

H. 4·4 cm., L. 7 cm., thickness 1·7 cm. Reg. 65 7-25 1

Red translucent amber, dull and cracked on the surface. One side is completely covered with yellow-brown patina; the other side has a few small patches only. The boring for suspension is just behind the foreleg and there is another boring which has been plugged at right-angles to it at the end of the piece.

The foreparts of the animal have been carved on two sides of a thin slice of amber. Both sides are carved with equal care and the style of carving in low relief reminds one of no. **71**. The modelling is simplified and highly stylised; the mane is a ridge without any indication of bristles (*cf.* no. **71**), and the tusk, ear and other details are carefully but simply carved. An engraved line marks the contour of the upper foreleg.

Presented to the Museum by A. W. Franks. There is no information as to where it was found.

78. Pendant in the form of a lion's head PLATE XXX

H. 2·9 cm., W. 2·4 cm., L. 2·8 cm. Reg. 72 6-4 1003

Red translucent amber, dull on the surface and with patches of patination. The amber was pierced across for suspension near the back. The lower jaw is mostly broken away.

The lion's jaws are open, the face is completely framed by a stylised version of the mane and the ears are carved very small on the flat surface behind it. The style is not unlike nos. **64–5**.

Purchased from Alessandro Castellani; from the collection of Prince Sangiorgio Spinelli (Detken, *Ambers*, pl. I D; which shows the pendant in a less damaged state).

79. Bull's head PLATE XXX

H. 4·3 cm., W. 4·8 cm., thickness (max.) 2·3 cm. Reg. WT 1452 (Old Cat. no. 11)

Red translucent amber, dull on the surface and deeply cracked. The lower part of the face is broken away and to judge from the surface, the break is a very old one. The amber is bored vertically, a rather thin boring, probably not the for bow of a fibula. There are several holes and cracks, of which one, just below the left horn, seems to be artificial.

The bull's head, highly stylised in detail, is carved from a regularly worked piece of amber. Between the short, horizontal horns the hair is shown by vertical grooving. The pair of horizontal grooves below the hair are probably meant to represent a thin fillet. The ears are rough bosses below the horns. The eyes are very large, of pointed oval shape framed by grooves. The rest of the facial detail has disappeared. Only the hair is shown at the back of the head, the rest of the surface is smooth but unworked.

Bequeathed by Sir William Temple; said to come from Armento.

80. Head of a goat(?) PLATE XXX

H. 2·8 cm., L. 6·6 cm., thickness 1·3 cm. Reg. 73 8-20 711

Red translucent amber, dull and shattered on surface with some slight patination. Extremities broken away. Suspension boring through an elongated bead-and-reel with another diagonal boring into it from the top.

The head is carved from a shapeless piece of amber with a deep cavity below the ear. The interpretation of the piece is not certain but the long horizontal ear, the beginnings of a horn on the top of the head (now largely broken away) and, perhaps, the root of a beard below the chin suggest a goat. The eye is large and round, the features well modelled. The style recalls the head-pendants nos. **54–60**.

This piece was purchased from Alessandro Castellani. It is not apparently one of the ambers formerly in the collection of Prince Sangiorgio Spinelli.

81. Pendant in the form of a ram's head PLATE XXX

H. 3·7 cm., W. 3·4 cm., thickness 2·5 cm. Reg. 72 6-4 1003

The amber is orange-red with deep patination and the surface is much broken. There is a flat surface, perhaps an ancient crack, on top of the right horn. Round the top of the head runs a double ridge and groove; the top is flat with a row of bead-and-reel in relief through which the suspension holes are bored.

The details of the head are carefully worked. The spiral horns are angular in section and marked by parallel engraved lines; the wool on the forehead is shown by cross-hatching. Ram's head pendants have been found all over Italy. There are examples from Sala Consilina (in Petit Palais, Paris), from Picenum (e.g. *MA* xxxv, 1935, p. 415, fig. 47), from Bologna (Zannoni, *Certosa*, Tav. XXXXVIII, 2), Marzabotto (Montelius Series B, pl. 109; Gozzadini, *Ulteriori scoperte* pl. 15) and

Metapontum (see under no. **61**). Seven ram's head pendants found with late black-figure pottery and other objects at Novi Pazar in Serbia are now in the National Museum, Belgrade. The bead-and-reel for suspension on the top of this example relates it to nos. **75–6**, and the style is rather different from the other rams' heads in the collection.

The pendant was purchased from Alessandro Castellani; it is not known where it was found.

82. Ram's head pendant PLATE XXX

H. 3·4 cm., W. 2·6 cm., thickness 1·6 cm. Reg. 72 6-4 1003

Red translucent amber, light opaque patina. Some surface cracking. The amber is bored for suspension just above the horns.

The head is flattened and the features elongated to conform to the shape of the amber. The wool on the forehead and side is shown by fine cross-hatching. The end is cut flat and round the edges are grooves and a ridge.

Purchased from Alessandro Castellani; no provenience.

83. Ram's head pendant PLATE XXXI

L. (overall) 3·8 cm., L. (of head) 3·1 cm.,
W. 2·1 cm., thickness 1·4 cm Reg. 72 6-4 1010

Red translucent amber with some surface cracking.

This pendant is put together from a ram's head pendant and an elongated biconical tube of amber. The tube and the ram's head obviously did not belong together originally. The amber of the tube is smooth and dull while the ram's head is patinated and rough. The head was originally of the same type as no. **82**, i.e. with a flat top grooved round the edge.

Purchased from Alessandro Castellani; no provenience.

84. Ram's head pendant PLATE XXXI

L. 2·5 cm., W. 1·9 cm., thickness 1·1 cm. Reg. 72 6-4 1010

Deep red amber with brown patina over surface. Most details, including the nose, chipped. The top is cut flat and has a bead-and-reel in relief which is horizontally bored, and partly broken away.

The pendant is very similar to no. **83**.

Purchased from Alessandro Castellani; no provenience.

85. Ram's head pendant PLATE XXXI

L. 2·7 cm., W. 1·7 cm., thickness 1·1 cm. Reg. 65 12-14 77

Deep red amber with deep patination. The suspension boring is through a half-round on top of the head.

The pendant is very similar to no. **83**. The features are hardly recognizable, through wear.

Acquired under the will of H. Christy; no provenience.

86. Ram's head pendant PLATE XXXI

L. 3·2 cm., W. 2·2 cm., thickness 1·4 cm. Reg. 65 12-14 76

Red translucent amber. The top is cut flat and has a V-shaped boring for suspension.

Similar to no. **83**.

Acquired under the will of H. Christy; no provenience.

87. Ram's head pendant PLATE XXXI

L. 2·6 cm., W. (max.) 2·2 cm., thickness 1·5 cm. Reg. WT 1461 (Old Cat. no. 20)

Red translucent amber, badly broken on the underside of the face. The boring for suspension, which is now blocked, runs through the moulded neck.

The head is more rounded and careful in detail than no. **86**. The style is related to the lion pendant no. **78**.

Bequeathed by Sir William Temple; said to come from Armento.

88. Ram's head pendant PLATE XXXI

L. 2·3 cm., W. 2·1 cm., thickness 1·0 cm. Reg. WT 1463 (Old Cat. no. 22)

Red translucent amber, badly pitted on the surface. The end of the nose is broken away. The boring for suspension consists of two diagonal holes in the top surface which meet in the amber.

Bequeathed by Sir William Temple; said to come from Armento.

89. Bottle pendants PLATE XXXII

a. L. 2·7 cm., W. (max.) 2 cm. Reg. WT 1473

b. L. 2·6 cm., W. (max.) 2 cm. Reg. WT 1473

Red translucent amber, dull on the surface with little patches of orange patina. Boring for suspension (partly broken away) runs from the centre of the top to the upper moulding of the neck.

These pendants are very similar to those in necklace no. **104** but flatter; the grooves and ridges on the neck are cut in the same way.

Bequeathed by Sir William Temple; said to come from Armento.

90. Bulla PLATE XXXII

H. 3·3 cm., W. 2·8 cm. Reg. WT 1471 (Old Cat. no. 26)

Red translucent amber, dull and cracked on the surface. The bulla is of roughly rounded shape, flatter on one side than the other. The upper section is rounded at the top and has two parallel vertical grooves cut at either end; it is pierced horizontally for suspension.

This kind of bulla has a very wide distribution in Iron Age Italy. A necklace of similar bullae was found at Padula (Lucania) (*NS* 1914, 403). There are many examples from Central Italy (*MA* iv, 1894, p. 381, x, 1901, p. 336, Narce and Aufidena; v, 1895, p. 134, Novilara; Montelius, Series B, pl. 171, Volterra). The bulla form has an immensely long later history; examples from Garlachsheim and other sites in S. Germany, date from the third to fifth centuries A.D. (*JRGZM* 7, 1690, p. 228 ff) are very similar.

Bequeathed by Sir William Temple; said to come from Armento.

91. Three bullae PLATE XXXII

a. H. 3·5 cm., W. 3·1 cm. Reg. WT 1472
b. H. 3·2 cm., W. 2·8 cm. Reg. WT 1472
c. H. 2·7 cm., W. 2·7 cm. Reg. WT 1472

The amber is very similar to that of no. **87**. The shape is like no. **90**.

Bequeathed by Sir William Temple; said to come from Armento.

92. Two large beads PLATE XXXII

a. H. 3·5 cm., Diam. (max.) 4·2 cm. Reg. WT 1474 (Old Cat. no. 27)
b. H. 3·8 cm., Diam. (max.) 4·6 cm. Reg. WT 1475 (Old Cat. no. 28)

The amber of both beads is deep red translucent, dull and cracked on the surface with a very light patination; both are chipped, perhaps deliberately, at the neck.

a is in the shape of a truncated cone with a flat surface and a neck at its narrower end. It is bored through vertically, the bore-hole being ·8 cm. in diameter.

b is similar but larger, the top is flatter and the horizontal section more angular. The diameter of the bore-hole is the same.

These large beads were components of necklaces; three similar ones in the museum at Bari (Inv. nos. 7680–3) were exhibited in the Mostra degli ori e argenti dell' Italia Antica (Catalogue no. 241).

Bequeathed by Sir William Temple; said to come from Armento.

93. Disc PLATE XXXII

Diam. 4·6 cm., thickness (max.) 1·1 cm. Reg. WT 1479 (Old Cat. no. 33)

Red translucent amber, dull on the surface. It may have been used as a bead on a necklace or on the bow of a fibula.

The disc is worked from a thin piece of amber; the surfaces are not worked flat but left in the natural shape. The disc is roughly circular and the bore-hole through the centre is 1·3 cm. in diameter.

Bequeathed by Sir William Temple; said to come from Armento.

94. Twenty 'cowrie shell' pendants PLATES XXXIII–XXXV

In the Register of Antiquities these pendants are roughly classed in groups according to shape and size. The groups are retained for the purposes of this catalogue and each is given a letter of the alphabet as a sub-division of the catalogue number, as follows:

a. one pendant	L. 3·4 cm.	Reg. WT 1464
b. ten pendants	L. (of largest) 4·2 cm. (of smallest) 2·9 cm.	Reg. WT 1465
c. one pendant	L. 7·1 cm.	Reg. WT 1466
d. one pendant	L. 5·5 cm.	Reg. WT 1467
e. five pendants	L. (of largest) 5 cm. (of smallest) 4·4 cm.	Reg. WT 1468
f. one pendant	L. 5·4 cm.	Reg. WT 1469
g. one pendant	L. 2·7	Reg. WT 1470

These pendants look like a simplified version of cowrie shells. They are egg-shaped, convex on one side and flat on the other with the flat side projecting to form a slight rim round the edge and widening to a broad pointed flange at the apex; a shallow groove runs the length of the pendant on its flat side. At the apex the pendants are pierced for suspension in various ways, either with two diagonal borings or a single horizontal boring across the apex. Presumably the pendants, graded in size, were strung together as necklaces; they were probably combined with figured ambers and head-pendants.

The pendants vary a good deal in shape, depending to a large extent upon the natural form of the piece of amber used to make them. *f*, for example, is very thin from back to front, and broad in proportion to its length; others are long and narrow. The largest is 7·1 cm. long × 4 cm. wide; the smallest 2·7 cm. long × 1·5 cm. wide. The amber varies a good deal in colour and in state of preservation.

A similar pendant of rather more regular form from Sala Consilina is in the Petit Palais, Paris; another is in the Vatican Museum without provenience. It has been noted that the frog no. **72** is the same basic shape as these pendants which probably served, as indeed did most of the Italic amber carvings, an amuletic purpose. A similar pendant forms the centrepiece of the necklace no. **106.**

All the pendants were bequeathed by Sir William Temple and are said to come from Armento.

95. Ring pendant PLATE XXXII

H. 4·2 cm., W. 4 cm., inner diameter 1·6 cm. Reg. 72 6-4 248

Deep red translucent amber, heavily patinated. The ring is slightly thicker below and narrows down sharply below the collar. There is no boring for suspension and if it was used as a pendant the string must have been looped round the collar.

The type of pendant occurs among ambers from early graves at Cumae (*MA* xiii, 1903) and is common on Iron Age sites in Italy.

The pendant was purchased from Alessandro Castellani; no provenience.

96. Ring pendant PLATE XXXII

H. 4·3 cm., W. 4 cm., inner diameter 1·2 cm. Reg. 67 5-8 714

Red translucent amber with slight surface patina and cracking. The ring thickens out below and has a flat collar at the top with scrolls engraved at either end, not unlike an Ionic capital in appearance. The pendant is bored vertically in a straight line through the top and the lower part of the ring.

Formerly in the Blacas Collection; no provenience.

97. Alabastron PLATE XXXI

L. 9·5 cm., W. (max.) 3 cm. Reg. WT 1451 (Old Cat. no. 10)

Red translucent amber, the whole surface patinated. Part of the neck and one of the lugs broken away. Suspension by means of a transverse boring across the rim and two diagonal borings from the top meeting the cross-boring.

A long thin alabastron widening towards the base is carved solid from a long piece of natural amber which originally suggested an alabastron in shape; some of the irregularities still survive. The alabastron has a neck and a flaring rim surrounded by a groove; there are two small lugs, one on either side.

Bequeathed by Sir William Temple; said to come from Armento.

98. Eight ribbed beads PLATE XXXI

Largest bead 2·2 cm.,
smallest bead 1·5 cm. in diameter Reg. WT 1484 (Old Cat. no. 38)

The amber varies in colour. The largest bead is light red; the others are darker with dull, lightly patinated surface.

Six of the beads are roughly plano-convex in section, the other two are flat on both sides. The ribbing is carefully carved and rounded on some of the beads; on the largest bead it consists of little more than a series of grooves radiating from the boring.

This type of ribbed short bead occurs widely in sixth and fifth century contexts both in Greece and in Italy. For an example from Trebenishte, see *OJh*, 28, 1933, p. 183. A very similar bead from a sixth century tomb at Cerveteri (Tomb III Mardi) is in the Villa Giulia Museum, Rome.

Bequeathed by Sir William Temple; said to come from Armento.

99. Three ribbed and three plain beads PLATE XXXI

The largest of the ribbed beads is 1·2 cm. in diameter;
the largest of the plain beads is 1·5 cm. in diameter. Reg. 65 12-14 79

Amber very similar to no. **98**. The beads are mostly damaged.

Of the ribbed beads, one is flat on both sides, the others are plano-convex; of the three plain beads, one, possibly two, was plano-convex and the third is a rough barrel bead.

Acquired under the will of H. Christy; no provenience.

100. Two ribbed beads PLATE XXXI

L. (of larger) 1·4 cm., (of smaller) 1·2 cm. Reg. WT 1483 (Old Cat. no. 27)

Light red translucent amber, the surface dull and patinated. The beads are barrelshaped, the ribbing roughly carved.

This type of long bead belongs with the beads nos. **98** and **99**. Examples occur in amber (e.g. Roscigno), glass and semi-precious stones.

Bequeathed by Sir William Temple; said to come from Armento.

101. Necklace of forty-two amber beads PLATE XXXVI

L. (as strung) 2·7 cm. Reg. 65 12-14 78

Deep red translucent amber; hardly any patination. Most of the beads re-polished, apparently by recent use.

The beads are mainly rather short round beads with rough-cut ribbing; a few are longer and similarly ribbed. There are two fragmentary plain disc beads (one of which is bored through the diameter), an oval long bead, a fragment of another bi-pyramidal long bead, and half a globular bead, all of the same type of amber. The beads are similar to **88** and **89**, and the presence of a bi-pyramidal long bead suggests that the collection comes from Italy.

Acquired under the will of H. Christy; no provenience.

102. Large bead PLATE XXXVI

D. 4 cm., W. 2·4 cm. Reg. WT 1480 (Old Cat. no. 32)

Red translucent amber, cracked and dull on the surface. The boring is blocked by some substance.

Bequeathed by Sir William Temple; said to come from Armento.

103. Ribbed bead PLATE XXXVI

D. 1·7 cm., thickness ·9 cm. Reg. 72 6-4 1011

Dark red translucent amber with light patina.

The bead is like the flatter type in necklace no. **101**.

Purchased from Alessandro Castellani; no provenience.

104. Necklace of fourteen bottle pendants PLATE XXXVI

L. (as strung) 10 cm. Reg. WT 1485 (Old Cat. no. 41)

Dark red translucent amber, dull and shattered with light patination.

The pendants are all similar with bulbous body and no base. On the shoulder are two or three grooves; the top is circular. The pendants are bored through the neck. Among the fourteen are two larger and more elongated examples; the smaller pendants include two varieties—squat and elongated, the squat shape being the commoner. A similar bottle pendant serves as the centre-piece of a gold and glass necklace in the Museum (*BMCJ* no. 1452).

Bequeathed by Sir William Temple; said to come from Armento.

105. Necklace of twenty-three round beads PLATE XXXVII

Largest (central) bead; diam. 5·7 cm., thickness 2·5 cm. Reg. WT 1481
Smallest ,, diam. 2·4 cm., thickness 1·5 cm. (Old Cat. no. 39)

The amber of most of the beads is bright red and lightly patinated. Five beads, including two large ones, are darker, and the largest is light in colour and rather more heavily patinated.

The necklace consists of twenty-three short round beads graded in size; the two on either side of the largest bead are flatter disc beads with carinated edges. The shapes are irregular, depending to some extent on the shape of the amber lump from which they were carved. The stringing is modern and there is very little reason to suppose that the beads formed a single necklace in antiquity.

Bequeathed by Sir William Temple; said to come from Armento.

106. Necklace of thirty-six round beads PLATE XXXVIII

L. (as strung) 37 cm. Reg. WT 1482 (Old Cat. no. 40)

Red translucent amber with light patina. The beads are similar to those of no. **105** but smaller.

Bequeathed by Sir William Temple; said to come from Armento.

107. Necklace of miscellaneous beads and pendants PLATE XXXIX

L. (as strung) 34 cm. Reg. 86 5-1 6

The amber is red and translucent, dull on the surface; several pieces are lightly patinated.

The necklace consists of fifty-one amber beads and pendants of various shapes and a fossilised nut(?). The majority of the beads are simple disc beads. The central pendant is a cowrie-shell amber like no. **94**. There are two rather unusual pear-shaped pendants pierced across the thicker end. Several bulbous bottle pendants are similar to no. **104**, with engraved lines below the neck and a round top. One long bead has horizontal ribbing. There are also one square bead and one irregular pendant.

The necklace was bought from the Rev. G. J. Chester and is said to come from Cumae. Most of the beads seem to be of S. Italian workmanship; the provenience, therefore, is not unlikely.

108. Bronze earring with amber bead PLATE XXXVI

Diam. (of ring) 3 cm., (of bead) 2 cm. Reg. 72 6-4 991

Red translucent amber, dull and cracked on the surface.

The earring consists of a double coil of bronze wire threaded through a central boring in a thin amber disc-bead. The bead has a carinated edge and a shallow concave surface round the central boring; the boring was originally round but has become irregular with wear.

This kind of earring with very similar beads is common in the Marche, but does not seem to be exclusively Picene (*cf.* Gjerstad, *Early Rome* ii, p. 91, nos. 7–8). Picene examples come from Grottazolina tomb 21, and Belmonte Piceno (several examples sometimes combining more than one bronze ring and more than one bead). A similar earring was found at Bisenzio (Olmo Bello, Tomb 22); it belongs to the eighth or seventh century B.C. but the ring bead is rather different. The type was apparently confined to central Italy.

Purchased from Alessandro Castellani; no provenience.

ROMAN

109. Statuette of an actor PLATE XL

H. 6·8 cm., W. 3·9 cm., thickness 2·4 cm. Reg. 73 8-20 714

Red translucent amber, dull and cracked on the surface with some patches of deep brownish-yellow patina. The head has been broken off and reset. The statuette will not stand up on its base; it could have been suspended by the two holes which now separate the feet and the stick of the figure.

The figure is that of a pot-bellied bald-headed old man. He is draped in an ample cloak which covers both arms and falls in a long fold at his left side. His right arm is bent at the elbow with the forearm brought across the chest. The feet and stick are attached to a flat base. The old man's head is inclined to his left; the features are carefully modelled—full cheeks, deep-set eyes and a snub nose. The ears are now broken off but were large. The top of the head is quite bald and is pointed at the back. With the minimum of modelling the forms of the body and the position of the arms are skilfully shown; the back is flatter than the front but the figure may be said to be carved in the round.

The statuette, with nos. **110–113**, belongs to a large group, all from Italy, which includes examples in Naples (Siviero, nos. 563, 565, 568) and Ancona (*Guida Ancona*, p. 356, Museum no. 5567); one of the Naples examples comes from Pompeii (*NS* 1890, p. 74). Another was found at Aquileia and similar pieces, including actors wearing masks, are known from other parts of Italy. The centre of production may have been Campania and most of the pieces were probably made in the first century A.D. (For other pieces see list of finds on p. 35). The bald, stupid old man, with big ears and a pot-belly is a character from the Roman mime.

This statuette with nos. **110–113**, was purchased from Alessandro Castellani; all five are said to come from Nola.

110. Statuette of an actor PLATE XL

H. 5·5 cm., W. 3·5 cm., thickness 1·2 cm. Reg. 73 8-20 716

Red translucent amber, cracked and dull on the surface. Some pitting and cracking. The head has been reset.

The character is the same as no. **109**, but the style of carving rather different. The amber is flatter, the details of the drapery rendered by sharper lines and engraved folds. Although not modelled in plastic form, the details of the drapery behind are shown by careful engraving. The head is well-preserved, and has a rather ape-like appearance. Like no. **109**, the feet are not in the round.

Source as no. **109**.

111. Statuette of an actor PLATE XL

H. 5·2 cm., W. 2·9 cm., thickness 1·2 cm. Reg. 73 8-20 717

Red translucent amber, dull, cracked and pitted on the surface, especially the back.

The figure is very similar to no. **110**, but better preserved. The feet are divided by a drill hole through the amber.

Source as no. **109**.

112. Statuette of an actor PLATE XL

H. 5·1 cm., W. 3 cm., thickness (max.) 1·3 cm. Reg. 73 8-20 718

Dark red translucent amber, dull and slightly pitted on the surface.

Very similar to no. **110** but with slightly different set of the head. The feet are divided by a drill hole.

Source as no. **109**.

113. Statuette of an actor PLATE XL

H. 6·8 cm., W. 3·3 cm., thickness (max.) 1·5 cm. Reg. 73 8-20 715

Red translucent amber with some pitting over the surface, particularly at the back. The piece has been badly broken and put together from fragments. The head has been reset.

The head has large ears but is not certainly bald. The figure was apparently leaning on a stick but the stick does not appear below the drapery. The stance is more upright than that of the others and the head, as restored, erect; the figure is taller and slimmer in proportions, otherwise in technique and style very similar to the others. The back is flatter.

Source as no. **109**.

114. Perfume pot PLATE XLI

H. 5·2 cm., W. (max.) 6·1 cm., Diam. (of opening) 2·5 cm. Reg. 66 4-12 3

Orange red amber, partly opaque, partly translucent; the surface highly polished. Some small patches of yellow patination. Slightly chipped but preservation generally good. A deep fault in the amber accounts for the high relief of the panther and the putto.

The pot is carved from a lump of amber of a general oval shape. The hollowing out and the turning of the concentric rings on the base were done on a lathe. A ridge on the lid fitted into a wide groove on the top of the pot. The present lid does not seem to fit exactly and is catalogued separately (no. **115**).

The relief depicts two putti vintaging. The vines with leaves and bunches of grapes are carved in low relief. The putti are shown in higher relief at the two ends of the oval. One stands in three-quarter view holding a bunch of grapes in his left hand and plucking a second bunch from the tree with his right. Beneath his arm and below the leaves of the vine is a large basket for the grapes. The putto opposite seems to be sitting on a branch of the vine, holding in his raised right hand a harvesting tool and in his left a small bunch of grapes which is being snatched at by the crouching panther below. In front of the panther is a two-handled wine vessel with ribbed body and neck.

This piece dates from the early second century A.D. Ambers of similar style are common at Aquileia and other Roman sites in Venezia Giulia during this period (*cf.* G. Brusin, *Gli Scavi di Aquileia* p. 223, fig. 136).

Purchased at the Castellani sale; said to come from Aquileia.

115. Lid of a pot PLATE XLI

Diam. 3·9 cm., H. (max.) 1·8 cm. Reg. 66 4-12 3

Red translucent amber. The lid does not in fact belong to no. **114**, but certainly belonged to a very similar pot. It has been beautifully turned with a series of convex and concave mouldings, engraved lines and narrow fillets. The handle is let into a recess in the top of the lid.

116. Perfume vase PLATE XLI

H. 9 cm., W. 7·7 cm., thickness 2·7 cm. Reg. 77 3-9 1

Orange-red opaque amber. The surface cracked and dull; patches of very deep pitting on the surface.

The vase is flat and pear-shaped. There is a small opening at the top in a circular recess and the interior is carved out to a depth of 6·5 cm.; the sides are thin. The sculptor has followed the general shape of the amber lump making little attempt to achieve symmetry. The handles of the vase are formed by two panthers climbing up the edge. On the body are carved vine stems and bunches of grapes in low relief with a large acanthus leaf at the base. The figures are carved with care though the proportions of the animals are unnatural; the style is altogether very similar to no. **114**. On the bottom a flat oval has been hollowed out; it may be secondary.

This piece is also a typical product of the workshops of Aquileia in the second century A.D.

Presented by Sir A. W. Franks; no provenience.

117. Lid of a perfume pot PLATE XLII

L. 8 cm., W. 7·4 cm., thickness 2·7 cm. Reg. 73 8-20 719

Orange-red opaque amber. The whole surface covered with a deep cracked yellow patina, which has destroyed much of the modelling.

The lid was similar in form to no. **118**, but is carved from a thicker lump of amber and most of the projecting portion has broken away. The diameter of the pot (4·7 cm.) to which it belonged was rather larger than that of no. **118**. The lid is in the form of a swan lying with his wings slightly spread and his head resting, apparently asleep. The end of the swan's head is broken off. Two putti are playing on his back; one is just emerging from beneath his left wing and the other is lying with part of his body on the right wing. Because of the patina it is very difficult to describe the modelling. There are fine lines on the swan's back; the principal feathers are sharply carved like the slats of a venetian blind. The putti were probably very like those on no. **114**.

The piece is good workmanship of the same class as nos. **114–116**.

Purchased from Alessandro Castellani; said to come from Nola.

118. Lid of a perfume pot PLATE XLIII

L. 7·8 cm., W. (max.) 6 cm., thickness (max.) 1·6 cm., Reg. 94 5-17 1

Orange-red translucent amber, with patches of opaque orange. Edges and extremities chipped.

The lid, from a small perfume pot, is in the form of a satyr head carved from a thin piece of amber. The features are delicately carved, the modelling of the eyebrows, nose, moustache and beard being particularly effective. The satyr wears a wreath of vine leaves on his head bound by a fillet. The pupil is marked by a single drill hole. The carving reminds one of the work of the ivory carver. The back of the head is worked flat; the mouldings fitting the lid into the box were neatly turned on a lathe.

This type of lid for a round pot is common, its shape allows a projecting portion which could be easily lifted. A very similar lid with a youthful satyr head is in the museum of the Maison Carrée at Nîmes.

Purchased from Mr. Forrer; no provenience.

119. Finger-ring PLATE XLII

L. (bezel) 6 cm., W. (max.) 2·7 cm., diam. of ring 1·7 cm. Reg. 84 4-9 3 (*BMCR*, no. 1628)

Orange-red opaque amber; some parts in the round and in high relief broken away.

The ring is described by Marshall (*BMCR*, no. 1628) as follows: 'Large amber ring with carved designs in high relief on the outside of the hoop and on the oblong bezel. On the bezel is Venus, standing to the front with a Cupid at her right shoulder and another standing at her left side. She leans her right hand on a steering oar(?) by the side of which is a dolphin. On the shoulders are a group of Cupid and Psyche and a figure of Cupid respectively. Underneath the ring is a figure of Cupid holding a cornucopia(?), parts of all the figures have been broken away.'

Marshall's date (fourth century A.D.) is too late; the ambers of this type seem to date to the late first century and early second century A.D. This example is probably early, perhaps late first century.

Purchased at the Castellani sale in 1884; no provenience.

120. Finger-ring

PLATE XLII

Diam. (of ring) 1·6 cm., W. (max.) 3·5 cm., thickness 1·2 cm.

No registration number (*BMCR*, no. 1627)

Light red translucent amber; dull and heavily patinated in patches on the surface.

This ring described by Marshall (*BMCR*, no. 1627) as follows: 'Amber ring having a flattened oval bezel with a circular plate of amber inserted within it. Carved in relief on either side of the ring respectively are (1) a nude figure of Venus with her hands upon her breasts, (2) a figure of Cupid, holding up some object over his left shoulder. Considerably damaged'.

For this type of ring see *OJh* xii, 1909, Beiblatt, pp. 69–102, figs. 68–9 (example found in a girl's tomb of probably Hadrianic date at Starigrad, N. Dalmatia) and *NS* 1933, p. 389. There are very many similar rings in the Museum of Aquileia, Udine and Este; the centre of production was Aquileia. For the amber rings from Rhineland sites, F. Henkel, *Die römischen Fingerringe der Rheinlande*, 1913, p. 151 ff. and Taf. LXII.

Bequeathed by Sir A. W. Franks; no provenience.

121. Die

PLATE XLII

A perfect cube of ·9 cm.

No registration number

Light red translucent amber. One side is badly chipped.

The numbers on the die are arranged so that opposite sides add up to seven; the units are marked by a dot within a circle, a common form of marking on Etruscan and Roman dice. This example is probably Roman. There are four very similar amber dice in the museum at Aquileia.

Source not known.

122. Pendant in the form of a fish(?) PLATE XLIII

L. 4·5 cm., W. (max.) 1·7 cm. Reg. ML 1904 2-4 1226

Orange-red opaque amber; light patchy patina over most of the surface.

The pendant seen from the side gives the appearance of a fish; the two projections near the pointed end would then be the gills and the disc at the other end, round which the suspension string was looped, would represent the tail. There is a double groove round the widest part forming a waist and this seems to have no obvious explanation. The object was presumably an amulet-pendant; and perhaps phallic in intention.

The pendant comes from the Morel Collection, the great part of which was found in France.

123. Pendant PLATE XLII

L. 3·9 cm., W. (max.) 2·3 cm. Reg. 1906 7-20 14

Light red translucent amber, cracked and dull on the surface.

The pendant is bell-shaped and carefully fluted. The rounded part at the top, above the neck, is perforated for suspension and the mouldings of the neck are precisely carved.

Presented by Mr. Pierce Mavrogordato; found at Olbia.

124. Pendant PLATE XLII

L. 2·2 cm., W. 1·3 cm. Reg. 1906 7-20 13

Orange-red opaque amber, well polished on the surface. The upper part of the pendant is bored across for suspension with a wide boring.

The identification of the subject is extremely difficult. It looks at first as though the lower part might represent an animal head and the piece is so described in the Register of Antiquities, but prolonged study seems to reveal a complicated phallic amulet cut from a rough piece of amber.

Presented by Mr. Pierce Mavrogordato with no. **123**; found at Olbia.

125. Collection of miscellaneous beads of stone, faience, glass and amber PLATE XLIII

Reg. ML 1904 2-4 1252

The stringing is modern and the beads are probably a complete miscellany. The better amber beads are disc or short barrel beads of red translucent amber, more or less cracked and patinated.

From the Morel Collection; no provenience.

TABLE OF CONCORDANCE OF REGISTRATION AND CATALOGUE NUMBERS

Reg. number	*Cat. no.*	*Reg. number*	*Cat. no.*
59 12–26 833	43	72 6–4 737	27*c*
65 1–3 46	35	72 6–4 737	27*d*
65 7–25 1	77	72 6–4 738	24*b*
65 12–14 75	55	72 6–4 738	26*d*
65 12–14 76	86	72 6–4 991	108
65 12–14 77	85	72 6–4 1003	78
65 12–14 78	101	72 6–4 1003	81
65 12–14 79	99	72 6–4 1003	82
66 4–12 3	114	72 6–4 1004	19
66 4–12 3	115	72 6–4 1006	12
67 5–8 714	96	72 6–4 1007	13
70 10–8 69	1*g*	72 6–4 1008	21
72 3–15 40	1*a*	72 6–4 1009	59
72 3–15 41	1*b*	72 6–4 1010	83
72 3–15 42	1*c*	72 6–4 1010	84
72 3–15 43	1*d, e, f*	72 6–4 1011	24*a*
72 6–4 248	95	72 6–4 1011	25*l*
72 6–4 620	23	72 6–4 1011	103
72 6–4 621	18	73 8–20 695	36
72 6–4 622	17	73 8–20 696	38
72 6–4 625	22	73 8–20 697	37
72 6–4 663 [739]	28	73 8–20 698	39
72 6–4 663 [739]	24*c*	73 8–20 699	49
72 6–4 663 [739]	24*d*	73 8–20 700	47
72 6–4 663 [739]	24*e*	73 8–20 701	48
72 6–4 663 [739]	24*h*	73 8–20 702	50
72 6–4 663 [739]	24*i*	73 8–20 703	44
72 6–4 718	20	73 8–20 704	45
72 6–4 719	16	73 8–20 705	52
72 6–4 723	25*a*	73 8–20 706	51
72 6–4 724	25*k*	73 8–20 707	53
72 6–4 725	25*b*	73 8–20 708	62
72 6–4 726	25*d*	73 8–20 711	80
72 6–4 727	25*f*	73 8–20 712	71
72 6–4 728	25*g*	73 8–20 713	42
72 6–4 728	25*i*	73 8–20 714	109
72 6–4 729	25*c*	73 8–20 715	113
72 6–4 730	25*h*	73 8–20 716	110
72 6–4 731	25*j*	73 8–20 717	111
72 6–4 732	25*m*	73 8–20 718	112
72 6–4 733	25*e*	73 8–20 719	117
72 6–4 734	27*a*	77 3–9 1	116
72 6–4 735	26*b*	77 8–12 1	40
72 6–4 736	26*c*	84 4–9 3	119
72 6–4 737	27*b*	86 4–1 1717	8

Table of Concordance of Registration Numbers and Catalogue Numbers
(continued)

Reg. number	*Cat. no.*
86 5–1 6	107
90 5–12 6	30
90 5–12 13	32
94 5–17 1	118
97 4–1 300	2*d*
97 4–1 301(?)	2*b*
97 4–1 302	2*e*
97 4–1 303	2*c*
97 4–1 304(?)	2*f*
97 4–1 709	2*a*
1906 7–20 13	124
1906 7–20 14	123
1907 12–1 432	7*a*
1907 12–1 434	7*d*
1907 12–1 435	7*b*
1907 12–1 436	7*e*
1907 12–1 437	7*c*
1907 12–1 438	7*f*
1907 12–1 439	7*h*
1907 12–1 440	7*g*
1907 12–1 441	7*i*
1907 12–1 443	7*j*
1907 12–1 445	7*k*
1907 12–1 446	7*l*
1907 12–1 447	7*p*
1907 12–1 453	7*m*
1907 12–1 455	7*n*
1907 12–1 458	7*o*
1907 12–1 465	7*q*
1907 12–1 496	4*i*
1907 12–1 497	4*j*
1907 12–1 498	4*k*
1907 12–1 499	4*f*
1907 12–1 500	4*n*
1907 12–1 501	4*e*
1907 12–1 502	4*m*
1907 12–1 504	4*a*
1907 12–1 505	4*b*
1907 12–1 506	4*o*
1907 12–1 508	4*h*
1907 12–1 509	5*e*
1907 12–1 510	6*c*
1907 12–1 511	6*b*
1907 12–1 512	6*a*
1907 12–1 513	6*f*
1907 12–1 514	6*d*
1907 12–1 515	6*e*
1907 12–1 516	6*g*
1907 12–1 517	5*n*
1907 12–1 518	5*l*
1907 12–1 519	5*s*
1907 12–1 520	5*d*
1907 12–1 521	5*o*
1907 12–1 522	5*k*
1907 12–1 523	5*j*
1907 12–1 524	5*t*
1907 12–1 525	5*u*
1907 12–1 526	5*m*
1907 12–1 527	5*q*
1907 12–1 528	5*w*
1907 12–1 529	5*f*
1907 12–1 530	5*g*
1907 12–1 531	5*h*
1907 12–1 532	5*c*
1907 12–1 533	5*b*
1907 12–1 534	5*a*
1907 12–1 535	5*i*
1907 12–1 536	5*p*
1907 12–1 537	5*v*
1907 12–1 538	5*r*
1907 12–1 541	6*h*
1907 12–1 626	4*l*
1907 12–1 641	4*d*
1907 12–1 642	4*c*
1919 11–19 14	9
1933 6–14 22	3
WT 816	11
WT 1049	10
WT 1335	15
WT 1442	68
WT 1443	57
WT 1444	54
WT 1446	46
WT 1447	58
WT 1448	72
WT 1449	64
WT 1450	73
WT 1451	97

Table of Concordance of Registration Numbers and Catalogue Numbers
(continued)

Reg. number	*Cat. no.*	*Reg. number*	*Cat. no.*
WT 1452	79	WT 1472	91*b*
WT 1453	69	WT 1472	91*c*
WT 1454	65	WT 1473	89*a*
WT 1455	70	WT 1473	89*b*
WT 1456	41	WT 1474	92*a*
WT 1457	60	WT 1475	92*b*
WT 1458	61	WT 1476	29
WT 1459	76	WT 1479	93
WT 1460	75	WT 1480	102
WT 1461	87	WT 1481	105
WT 1462	66	WT 1482	106
WT 1463	88	WT 1483	100
WT 1464	94*a*	WT 1484	98
WT 1465	94*b*	WT 1485	104
WT 1466	94*c*		
WT 1467	94*d*	H 30	31
WT 1468	94*e*	H 32	33
WT 1469	94*f*	H 33	34
WT 1470	94*g*		
WT 1471	90	ML 1904 2–4 1226	122
WT 1472	91*a*	ML 1904 2–4 1252	125

I. INDEX OF PROVENIENCES

Catalogue numbers are given in bold type

II. INDEX OF DONORS, ETC.

III. INDEX OF AMBER FINDS

IV. GENERAL INDEX

PLATES I – XLIII

The scale of the plates is 1 : 1 except in a few cases where it has been necessary to reduce it; in these cases the scale is given on the plate.

e

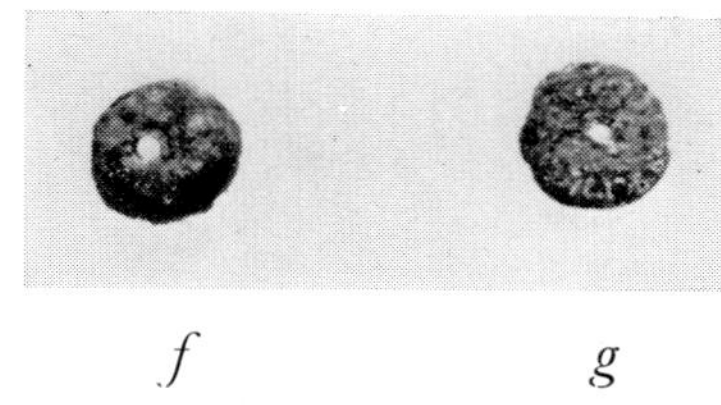

c *d* *b* *f* *g*

a

1

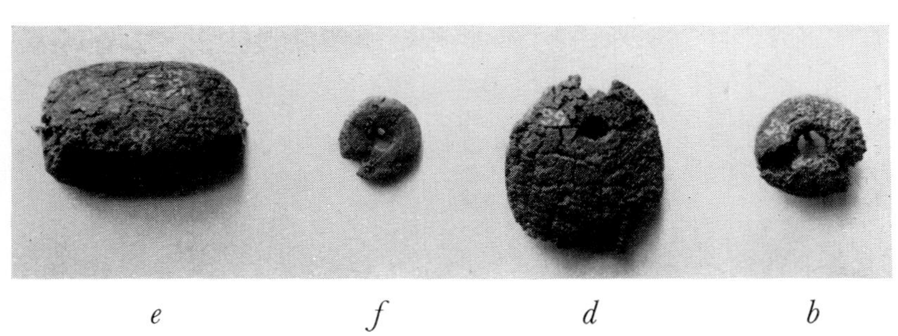

e *f* *d* *b* *c* *a*

2

3

PLATE II

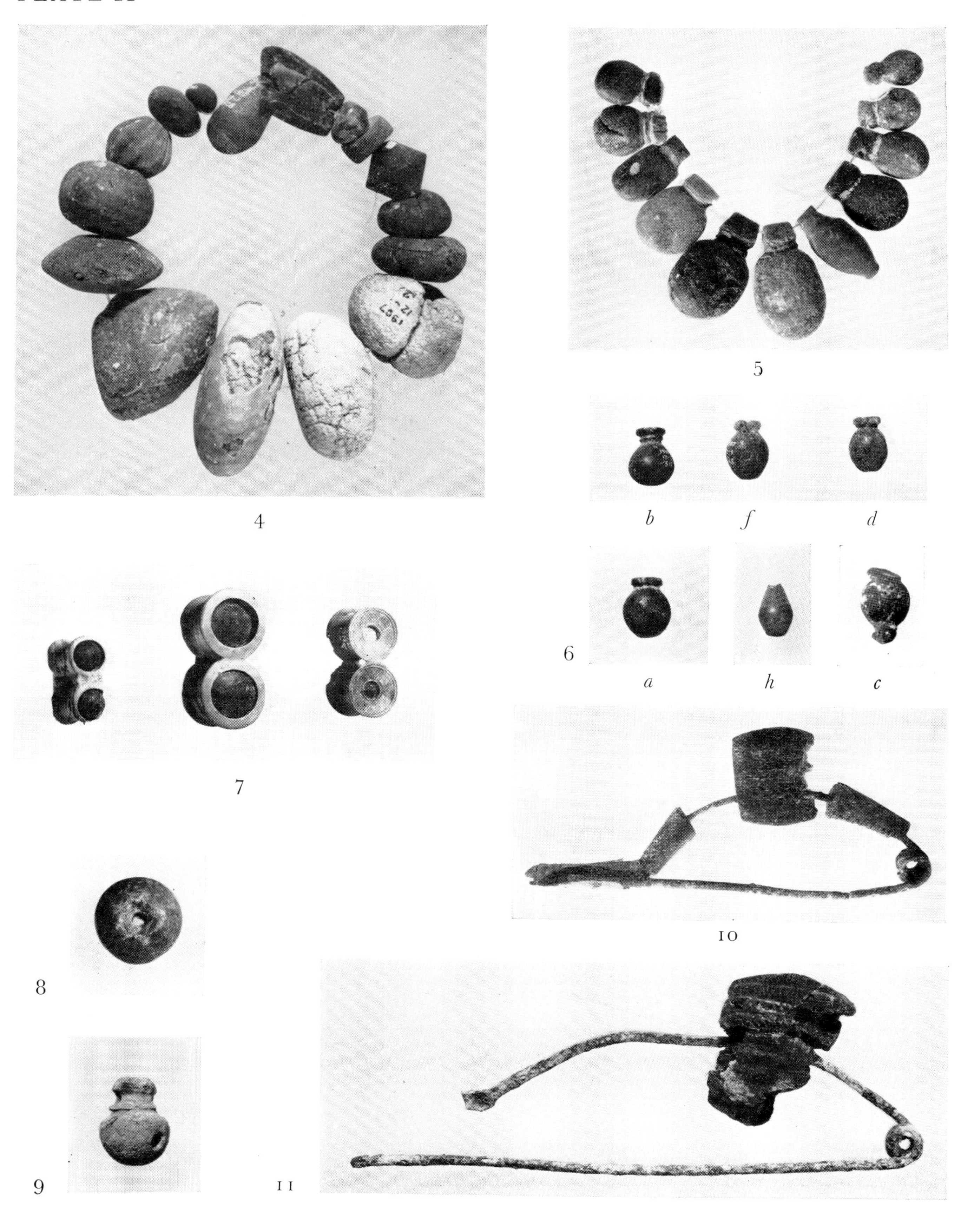

4

5

6

b *f* *d*

a *h* *c*

7

8

9

10

11

PLATE III

14

12

12

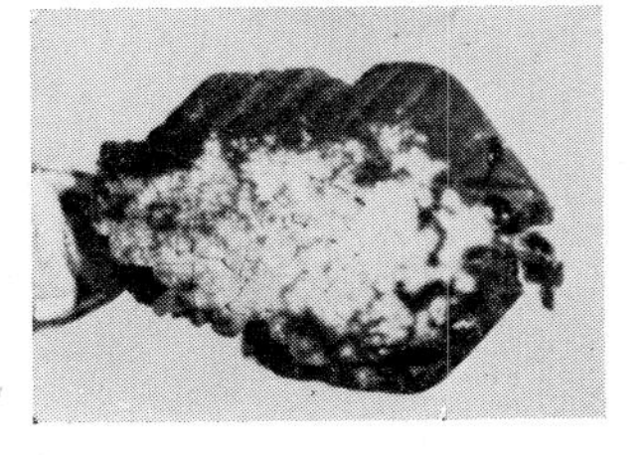

15

13

17
16

18

19

Scale 1 : 2

20 Scale 2:3

PLATE VIII

21

22

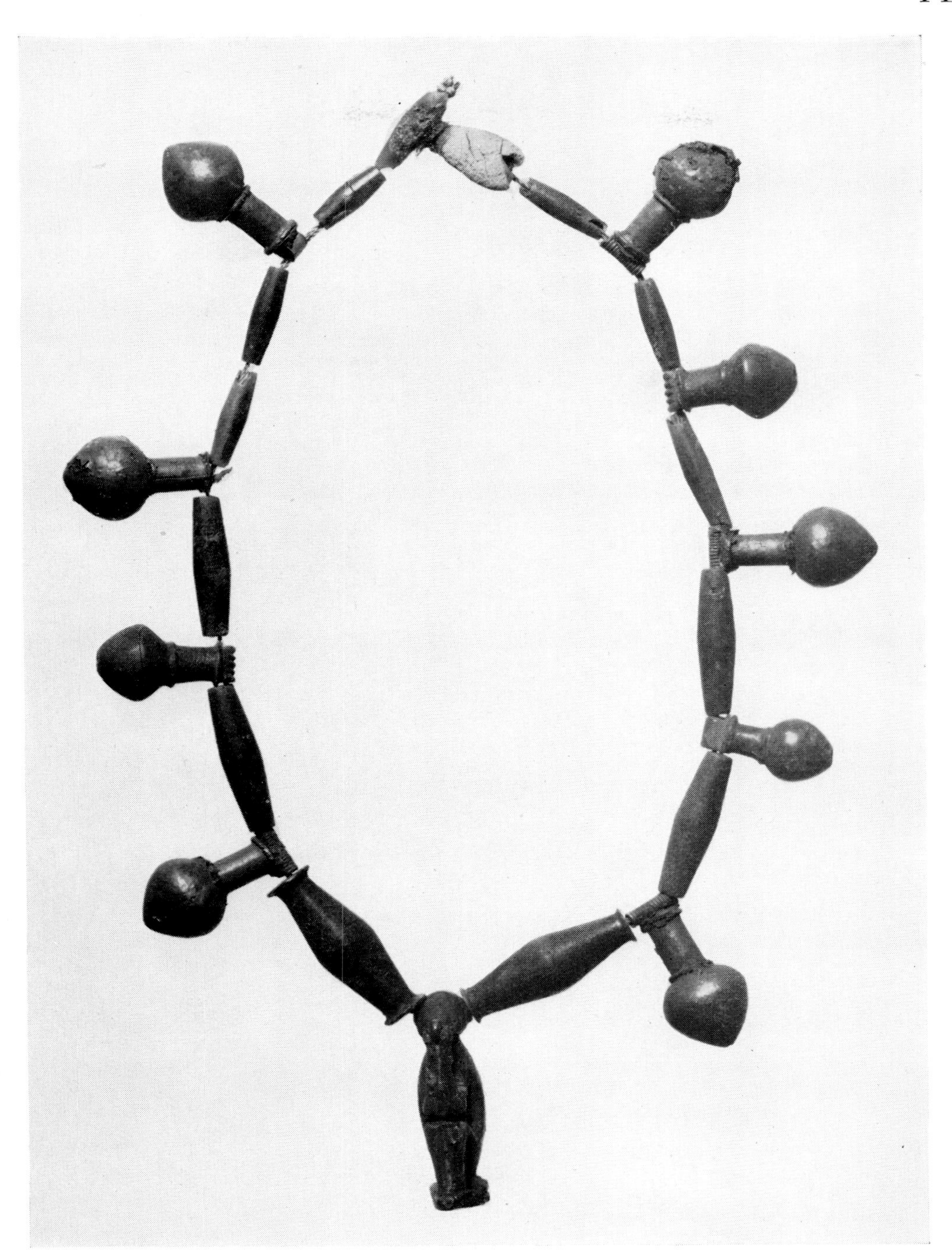

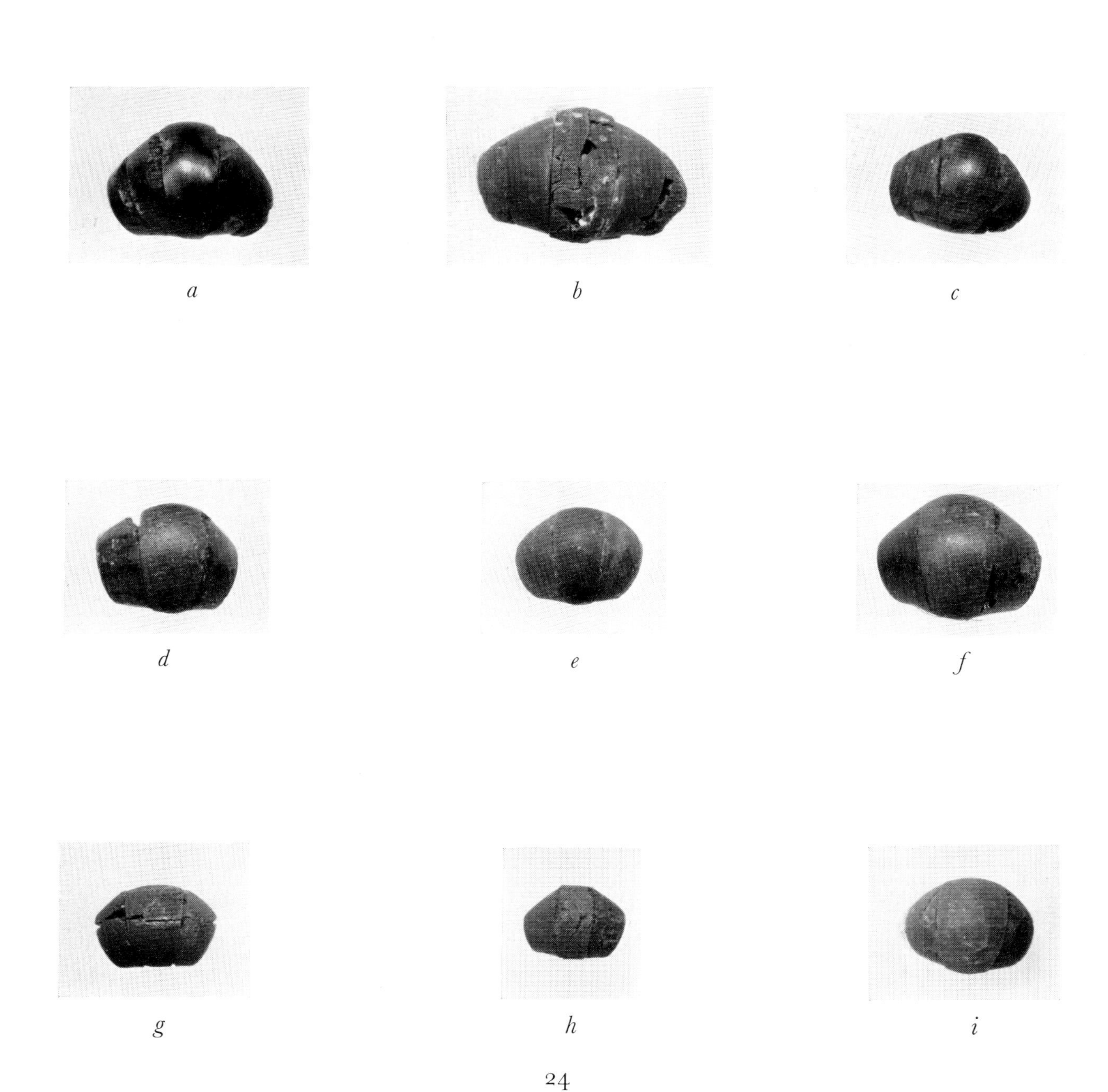

a *b* *c*

d *e* *f*

g *h* *i*

a *b*

c *d* *e*

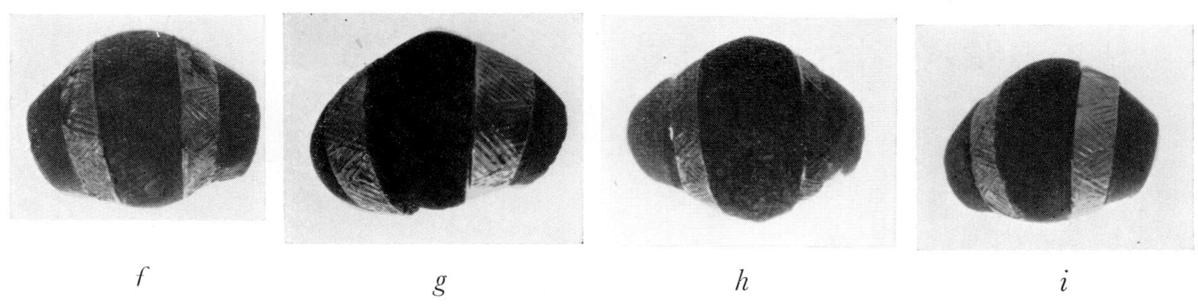

f *g* *h* *i*

i *k* *l* *m*

PLATE XII

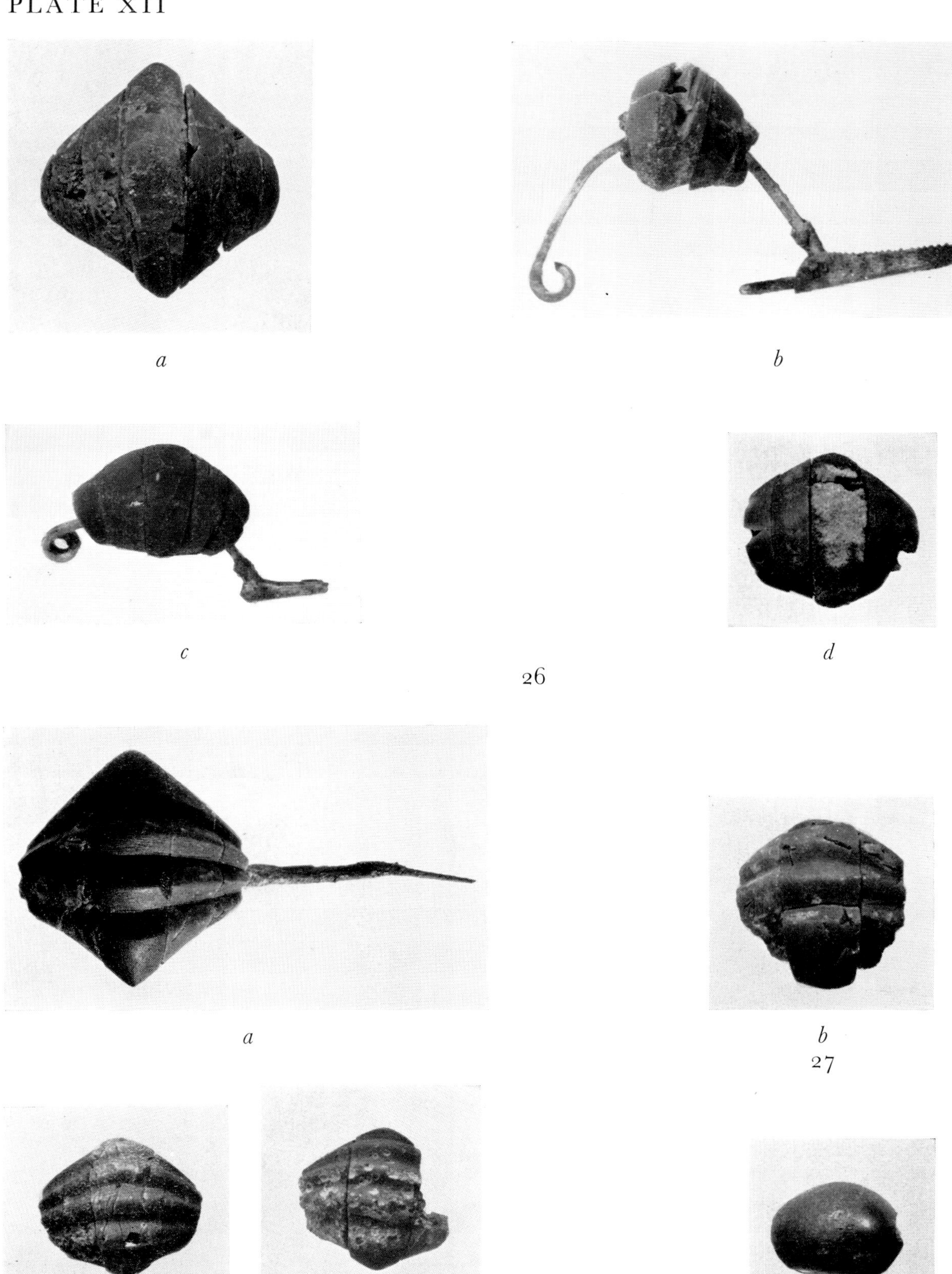

a *b*

c *d*

26

a *b*

27

c *d*

27

28

a *b* *c*

29

32

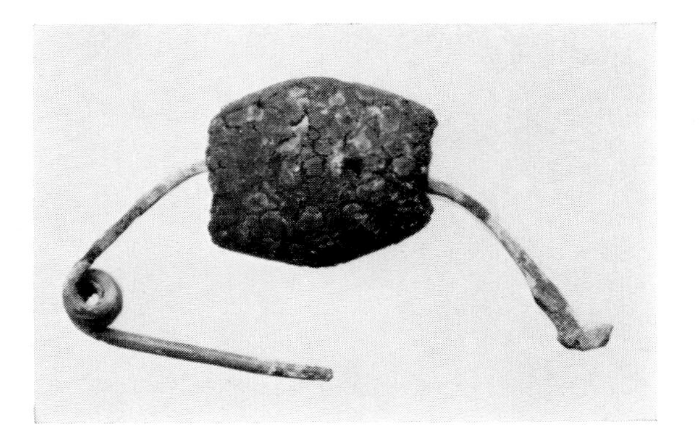

34

33

PLATE XIV

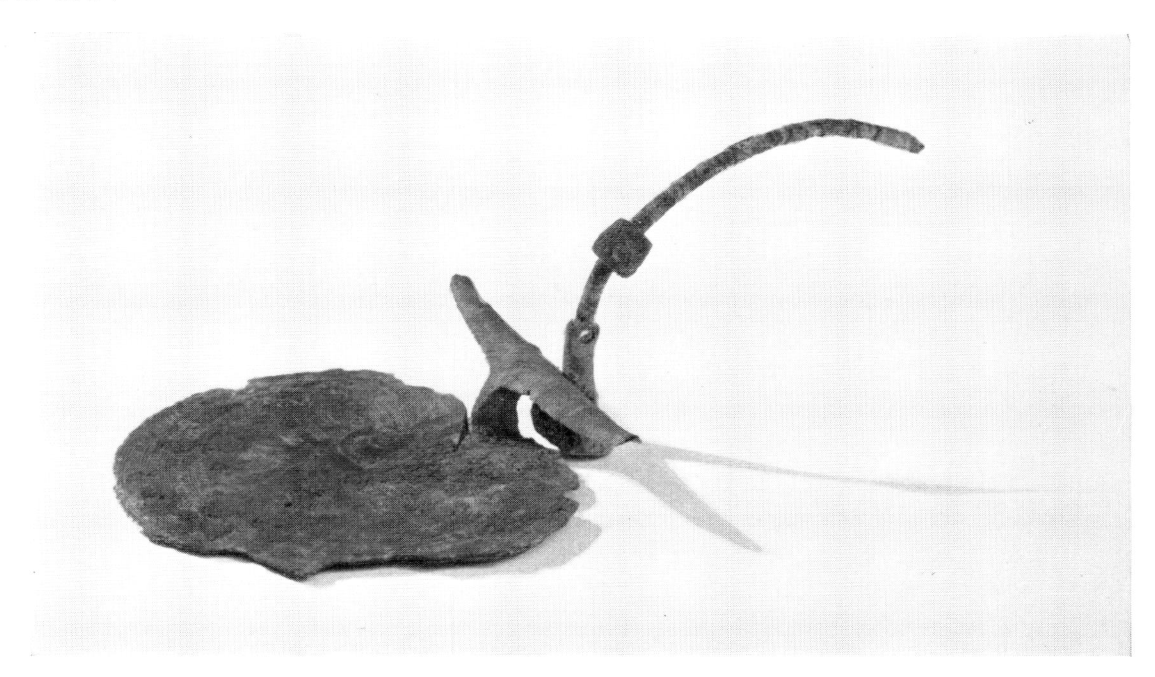

30

31

35

PLATE XVI

Scale 10:11

36

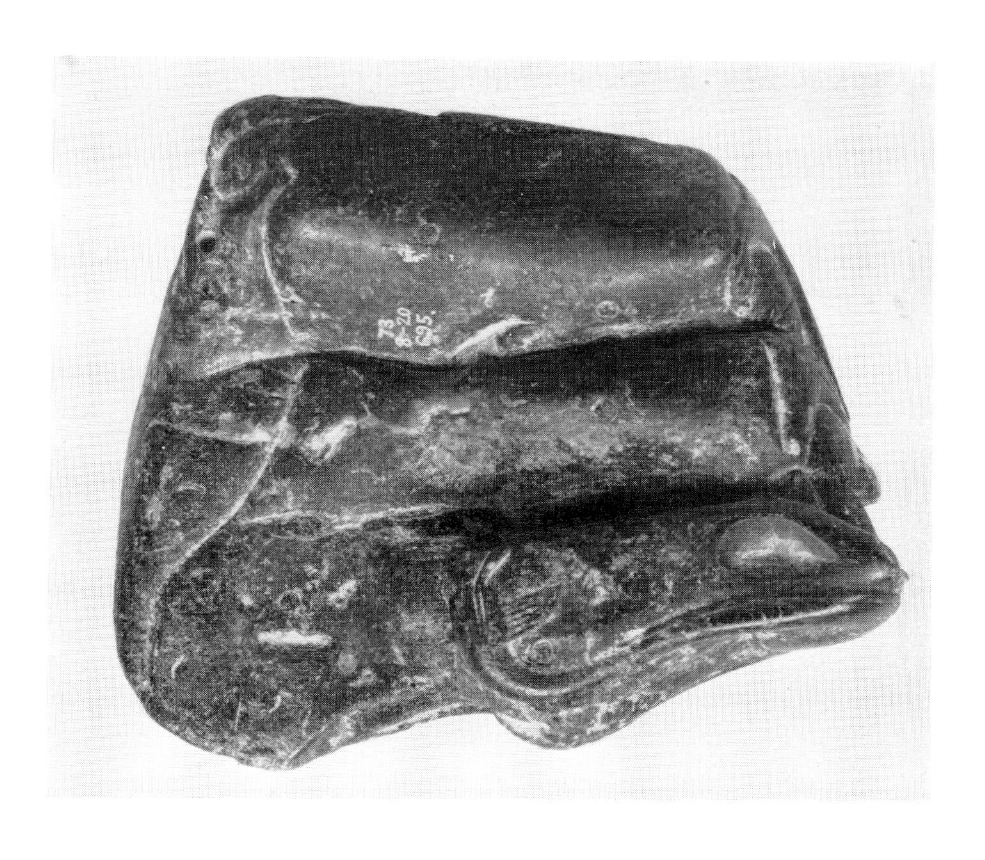

PLATE XVII

37

39

40

37

37

a

38

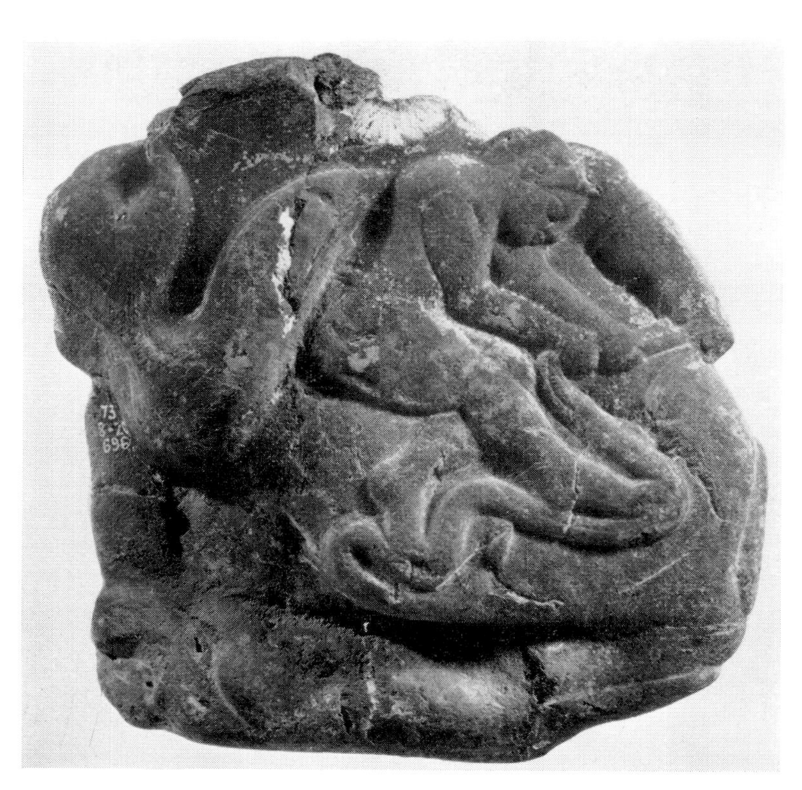

b

38

41

42

43

43

PLATE XX

44

45

46

47

48

49

50

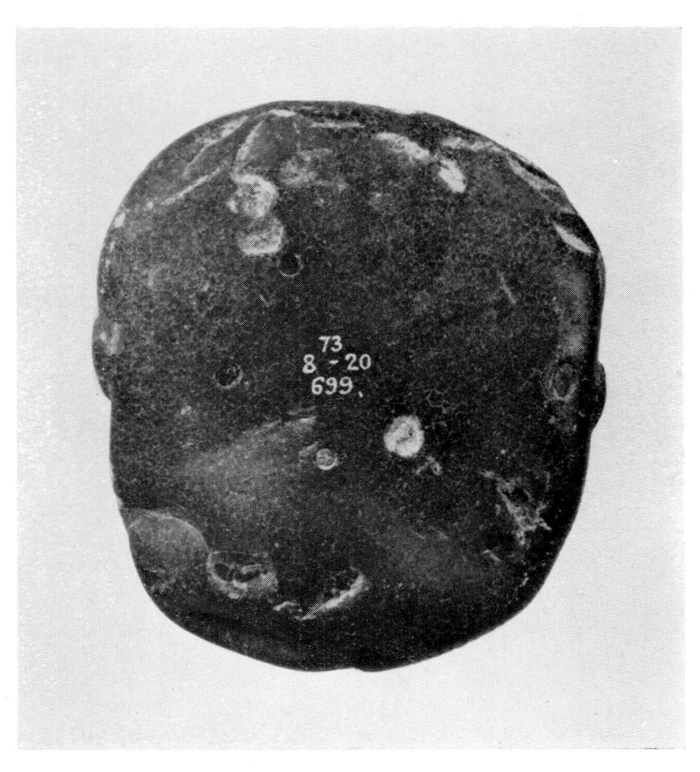

49

PLATE XXII

51

51

52

53

54

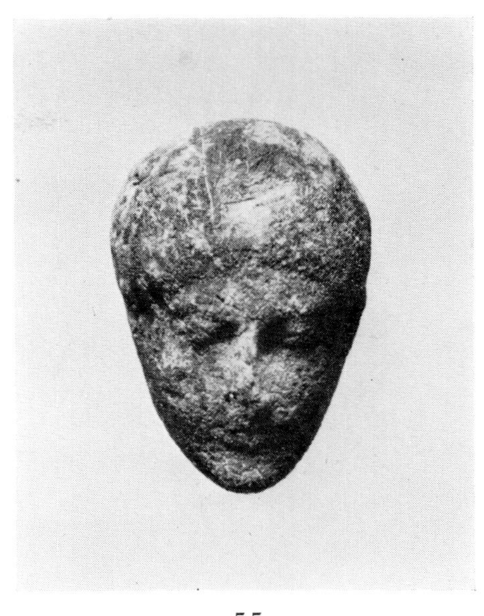

55

56

57

58

59

60

61

62

63

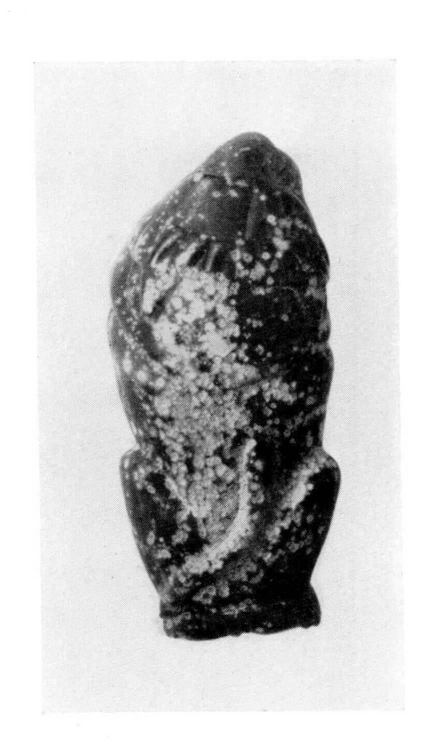

64

65

65

66

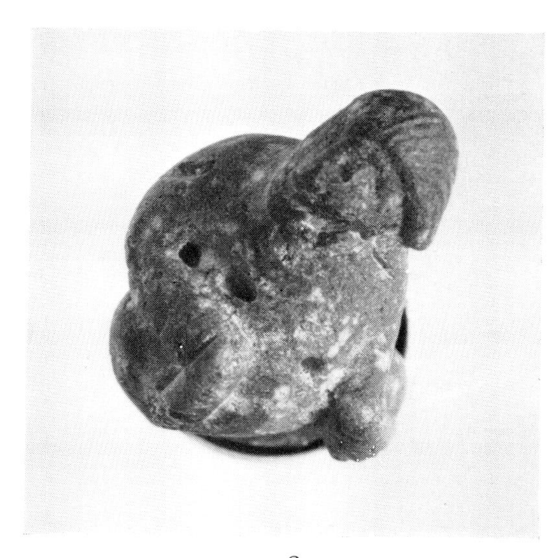

67

67

68

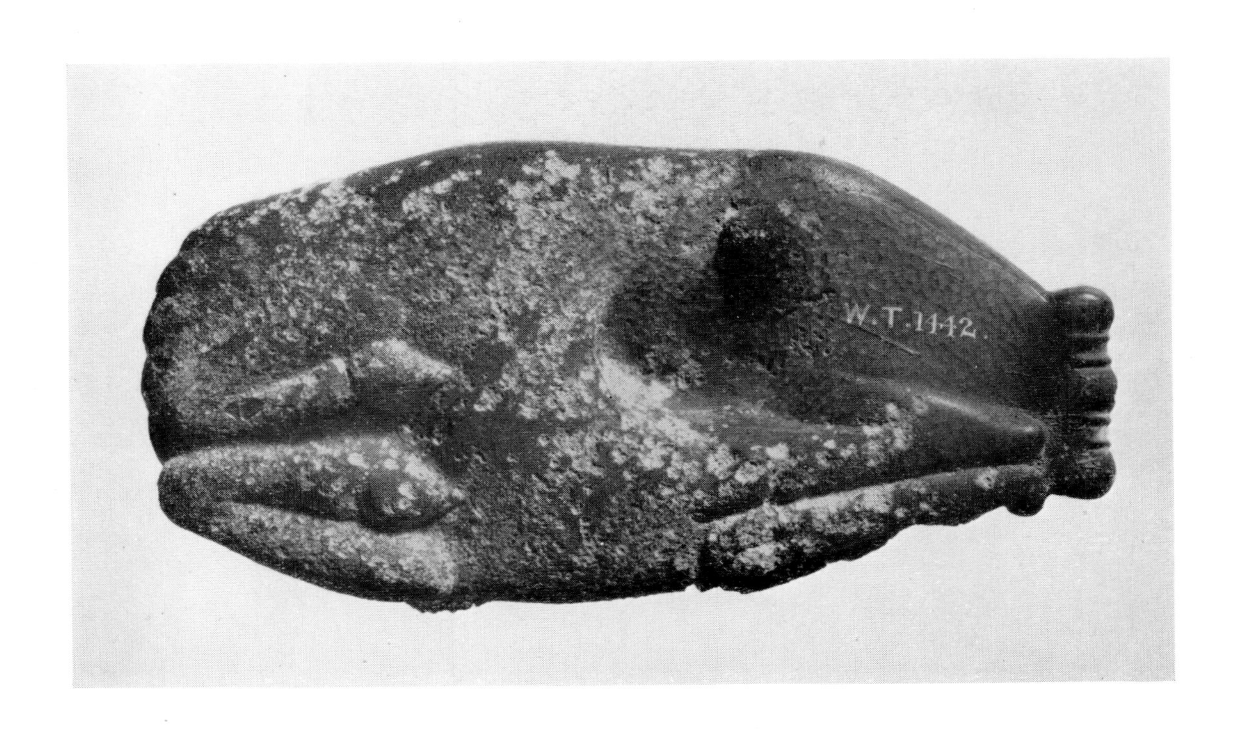

69

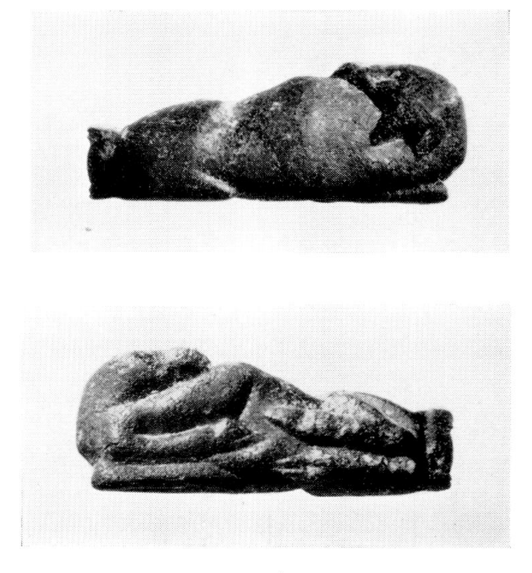

70

71

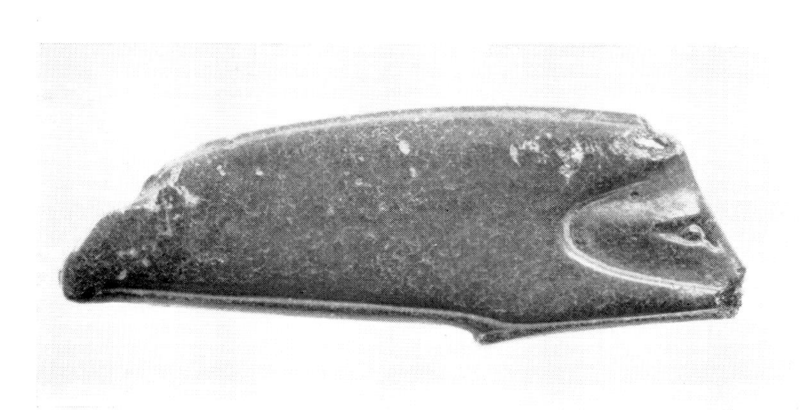

72

73

74

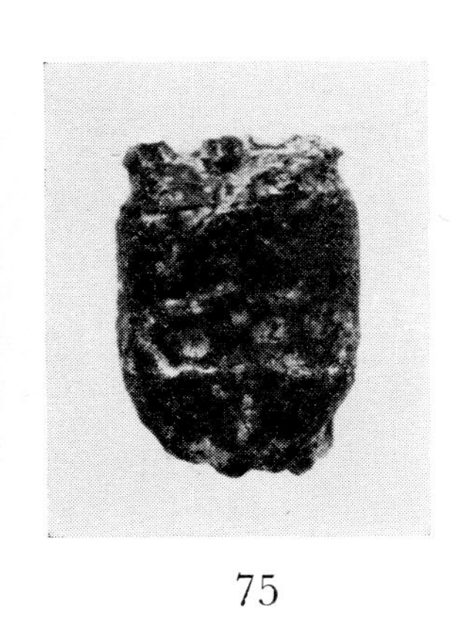

75

76

77

PLATE XXX

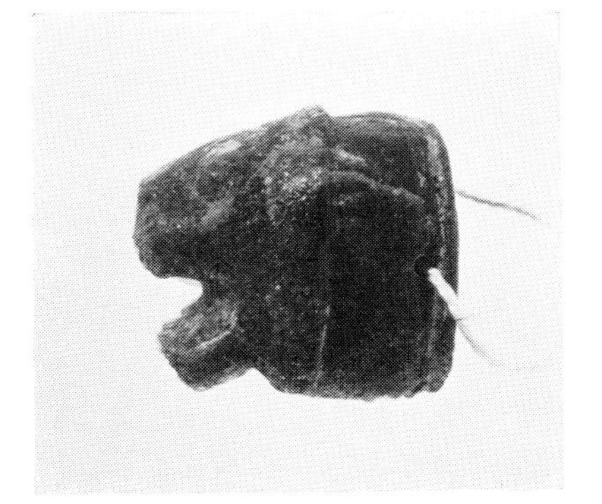

78

79

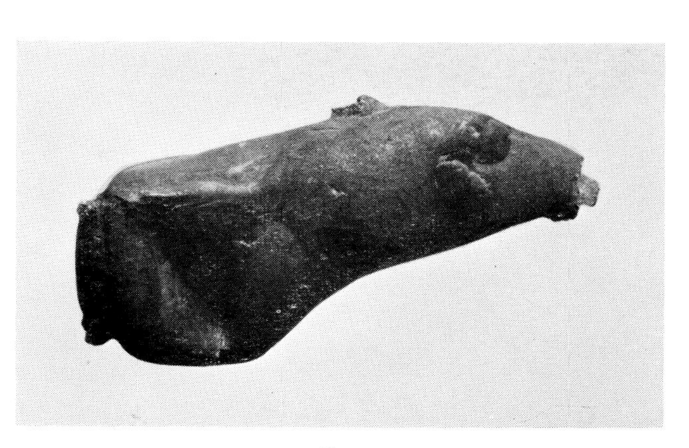

80

81

82

86 83 87

85 84 88

97 98 99 100

PLATE XXXII

89*a*

89*b*

b *a*

92

90

a *b* *c*

91

93

96

95

PLATE XXXIII

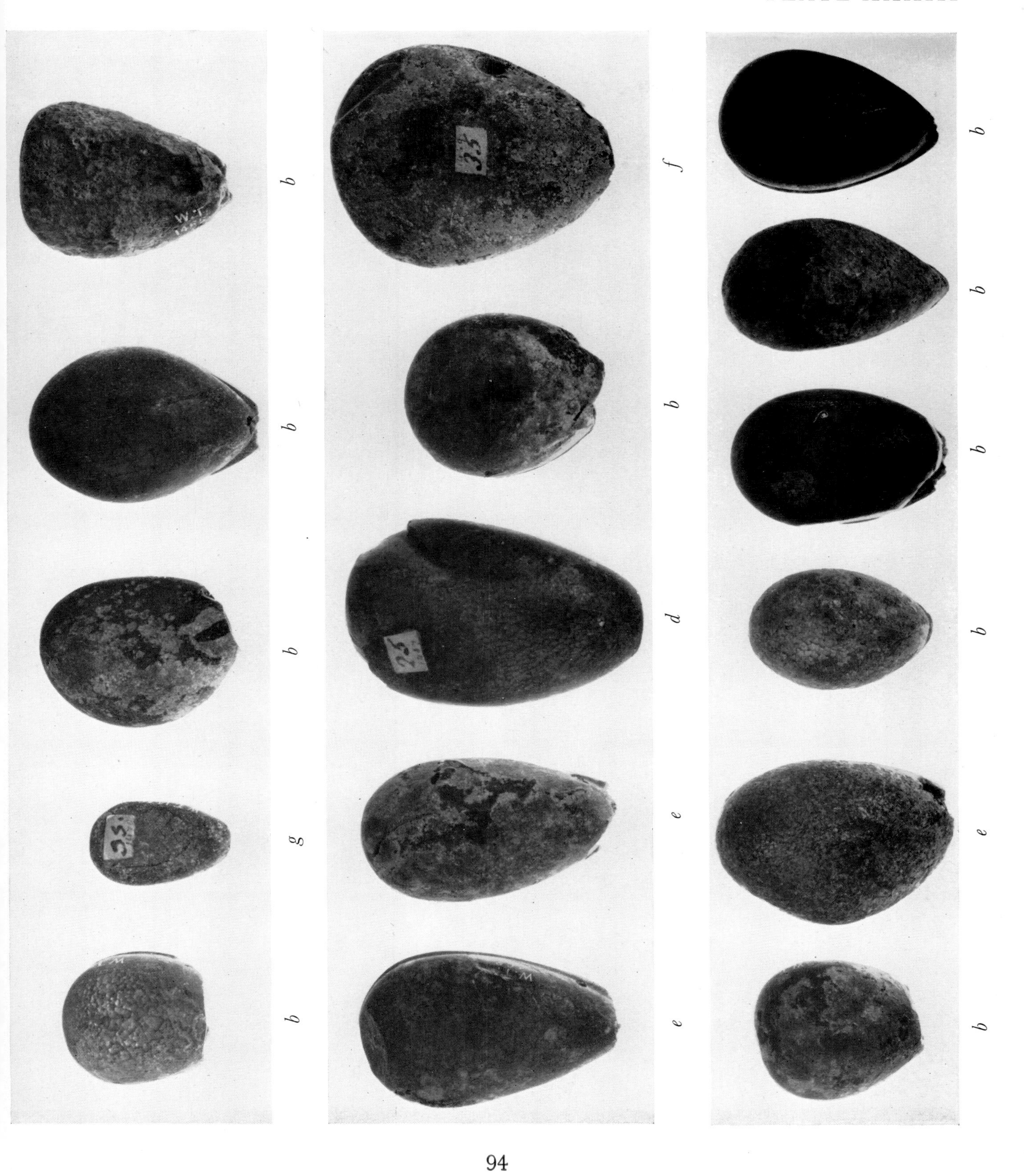

PLATE XXXIV

e *a* *e*

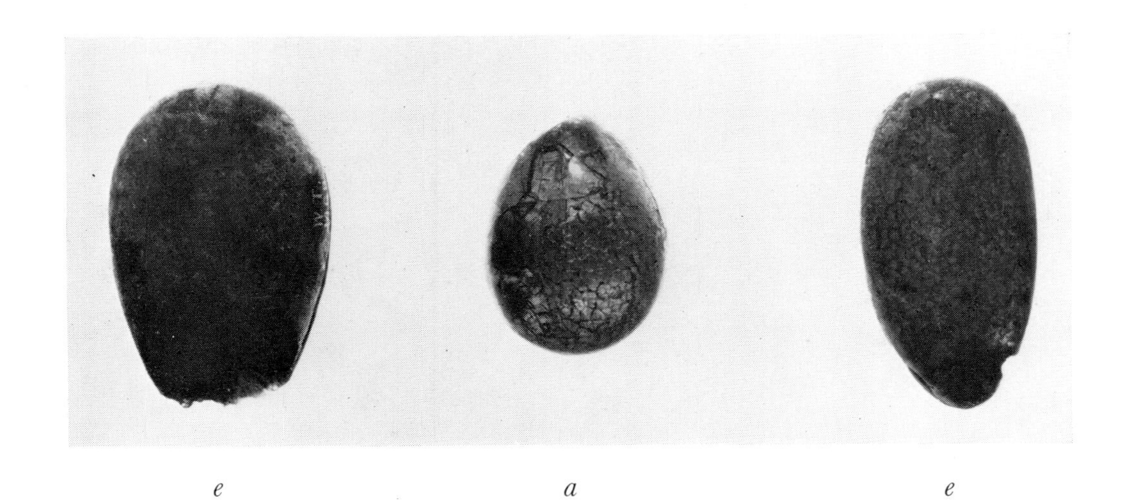

e *a* *e*

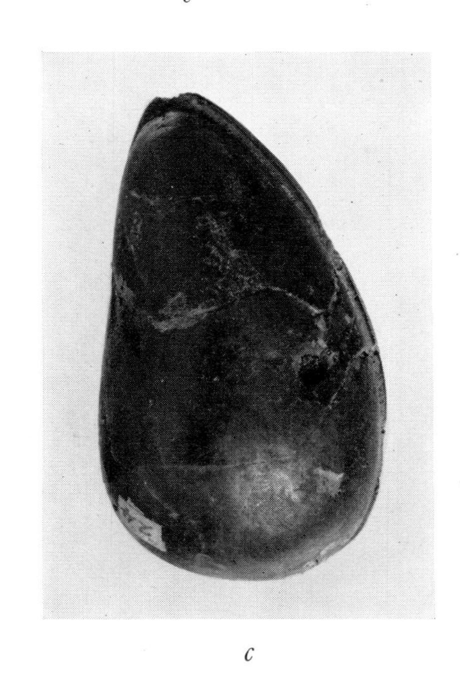

c

c

PLATE XXXVI

102

104

108

103

101

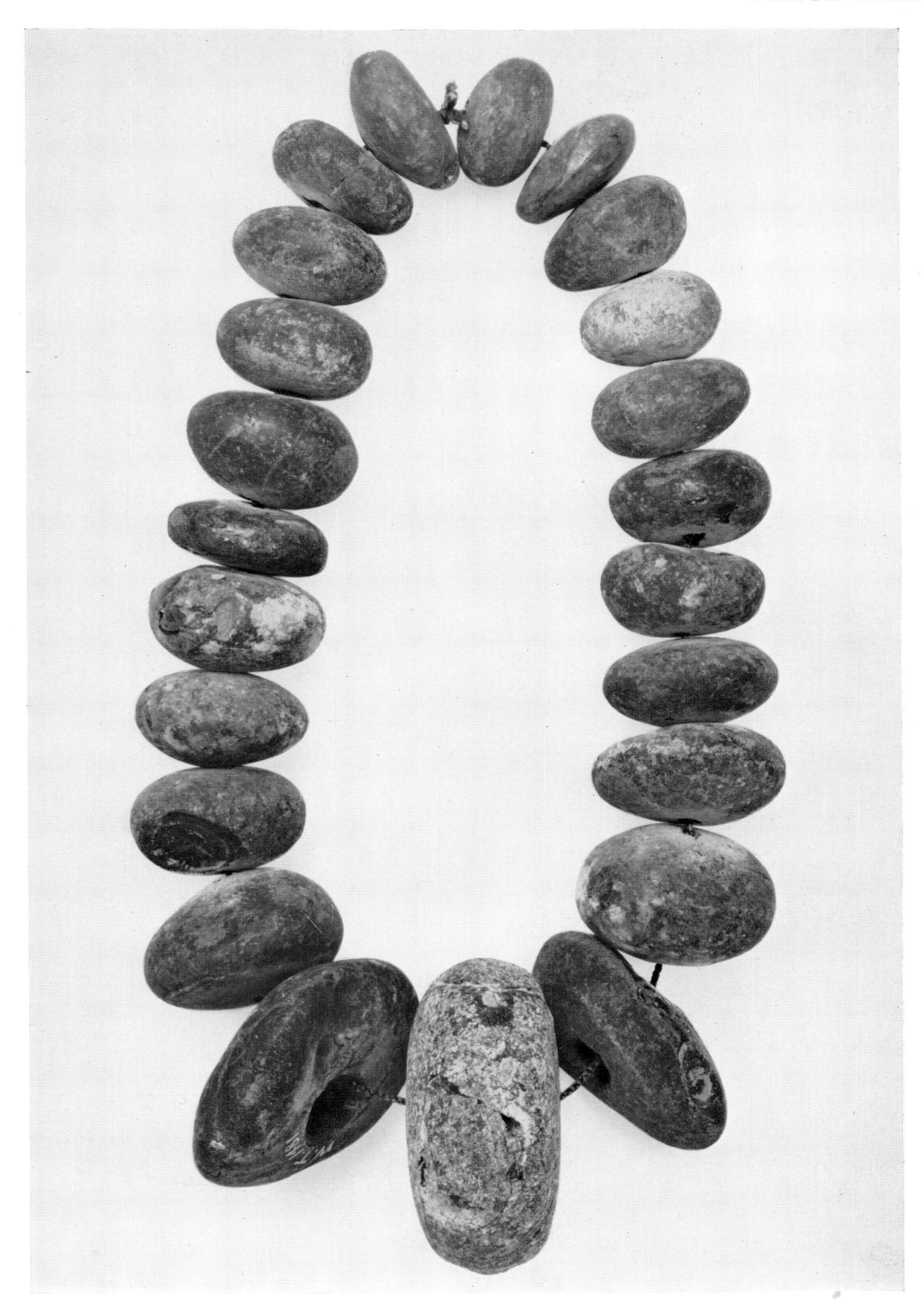

PLATE XXXVIII

PLATE XL

109

113

110

111

112

110

116

115

114

114

PLATE XLII

119

117

121

123

119

124

120

118

118

125

122